ANIMAL MARCH

To Dylan
Who gives a shit!
Join the March
and save the 'Glades
Kim Frances Lee

Kim Frances Lee

Illustrated by Tyler Amato

ANIMAL MARCH

Cover design and illustrations by Tyler Amato

ISBN: 978-0-9966223-0-1

To Stuart Lee,
who is always there for me

Contents

ANIMAL MARCH

Kim Frances Lee

Illustrated by Tyler Amato

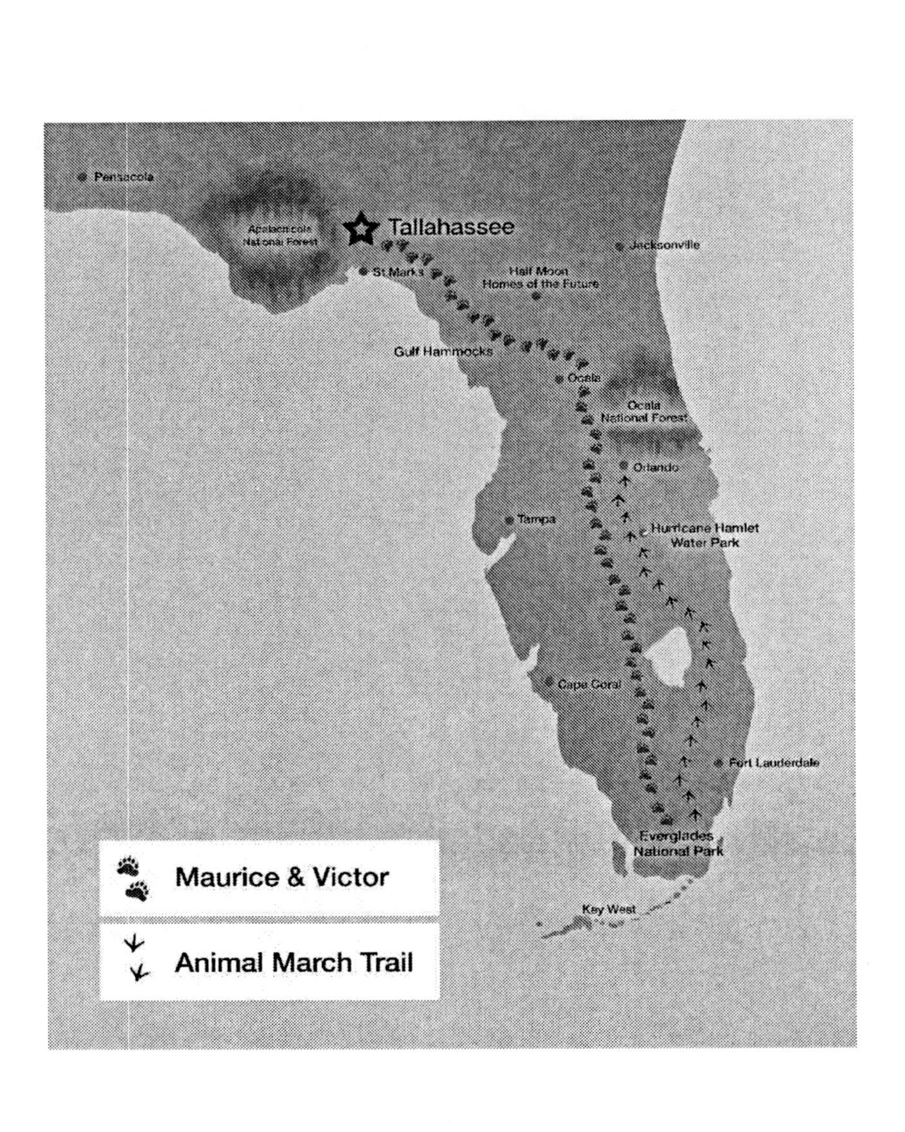
Pensacola
Apalachicola
National Forest
Tallahassee
Jacksonville
St Marks
Half Moon
Homes of the Future
Gulf Hammocks
Ocala
Ocala
National Forest
Orlando
Tampa
Hurricane Hamlet
Water Park
Cape Coral
Fort Lauderdale
Everglades
National Park
Key West
Maurice & Victor
Animal March Trail

Chapter 1

A Vulture, a Machine, and a Plan

The ground shook from the weight of the heavy bulldozer. Dirt, twigs, and small pine cones vibrated across the ground, bouncing up and down while creating a cloud of dust.

Bu Zard coughed and waved his wings in front of his beak to clear the air, then stepped back to reassess the situation. He did not have to be here facing this large, metal monster of a machine. In fact, he could be anywhere he wanted, because he was a vulture and he could fly. He was an expert at flying and had graduated as one of the top students in his class at Vulture Technical School (the advanced school of aerodynamic flight for gifted vultures).

Bu Zard looked around at the small group of animals that had joined him to get involved with—as his family and friends were so fond of telling him—"things no self-respecting vulture would dream of." A self-respecting vulture spent his life cleaning up the decaying flesh of dead animals. But not Bu Zard. He had taken the cleaning thing to a whole different level. He was on a one-vulture mission to clean up the Everglades and return it to its former pristine beauty. Flying away was definitely not an option at the moment. He had committed himself to a cause.

"Spread out a little," he said. "I want our group to look really big and strong. Or at least big enough to hold off that bulldozer."

The vulture was not as tall as the blue heron to his right and not as angry-looking as the black bear on his left, but he was the self-appointed leader of the group and, for the moment, felt as if he had everything under control.

The pine forest they stood in was the last barrier—at this particular place—between Everglades National Park and the large agricultural farms, commercial nurseries, and busy neighborhoods of South Florida.

And Bu Zard's small group of animal friends was the last barrier between the pine forest and a fourteen-ton bulldozer.

The operator of the massive metal machine sat inside the cab, talking on the phone and waving his arms as if the person he spoke to could see him. Behind the bulldozer, a group of men paced back and forth beside their trucks while waiting to start work on the new housing development.

Both the bear and the heron had to step to the side as the vulture stretched his wings even farther, showing the brown and silver undersides in an attempt to look *big and strong*.

"We just need to hold them back for a few more minutes. The other animals should be here any minute now. Yep, any minute now." The vulture looked back over his shoulder and scanned the forest behind him.

The blue heron tried to take another step to the right, but a family of raccoons blocked her movements by gathering around her feet as if she were their protector.

"The other animals should be here any minute now. Yep, any minute now." The vulture looked back over his shoulder and scanned the forest behind him.

"Are you sure about that?" asked the bear. "You had actual confirmation that other animals from the Everglades would be here to stop this bulldozer from destroying my home?"

"Well, technically . . . ," said the vulture, dropping his wings to his sides. "Technically . . . , not confirmed. But a few said they would try, and I can't believe that *none* of them will show."

"*Try*, Bu Zard?" squawked the blue heron as she stepped over a raccoon to face the turkey vulture. "*A few* said they'd *try*? You told me we would *not* be alone and we'd have plenty of support if we came here today. You're going to get us in trouble."

Bu Zard watched his friend glance around anxiously, probably looking for the animals that he promised and *hoped* were coming to their aid. The blue heron paused, looking at one particular spot for a moment, and then resumed her scanning of the forest.

"They'll be here, Frieda. Just trust me. This is important," Bu Zard said.

He watched as the operator of the bulldozer, a man in a white hardhat, turned off the phone he had been talking into and put it into his right shirt pocket.

"Okay, Bu Zard," the man yelled. "You've got to clear out of here now. Take all your little friends and leave the construction area. You have to go home *now* because I have a job to do, and my bosses are sick of you holding us up."

"You can't make us leave!" Bu Zard yelled back.

Frieda popped Bu Zard in the back of his head with her wing. "Are you trying to make him mad?" she asked.

"I'm warning you, Bu Zard," shouted the man. "Clear out now!"

"Is he threatening us?" asked Frieda. Then she answered her own question. "I think he's threatening us."

"That man is not going to run a bulldozer over a group of animals. This is a peaceful protest," said Bu Zard, addressing all the animals present. "Besides, it's against the law to harm us. We're protected by the government, or at least I am. . . . I think black bear and blue heron are protected too." He glanced down at Frieda's feet where the raccoon family huddled. "I don't know about you raccoons though. Not all animals are protected. We'll need to check before we send you out to protest on your own. We don't want—"

The operator of the mega-ton machine suddenly throttled the engine to full power.

Frieda stepped back, tripping over one of the baby raccoons that had positioned itself behind her.

"It's all right, Frieda," the vulture yelled. "It's just for show."

The bulldozer operator raised the eight-foot blade, which had a large half-moon printed in the center of it, a few feet off the ground.

Beep, beep, beep, the bulldozer signaled that it was backing up.

Bu Zard pointed a wing at the machine and yelled, "See he's going to leave. He, he—"

The aggressive bulldozer operator slammed the blade into the earth, cutting a deep line though the pine needles covering the ground and breaking the surface of the soil.

The operator put the machine in forward. Heavy smoke from the diesel that fueled the monster machine poured from the smoke stack. The blade pushed the ground up in the front as the giant belts that moved the machine forward rolled over small pine trees.

"Bu Zard, he's not going to stop!" squawked Frieda. She flapped her wings in panic and flew away.

Bu Zard threw up his wings to concede the ground to the giant piece of metal. "Move back," he cried. "Move back!"

But the baby raccoons were too panicked to move. They pressed their tiny faces into the pine needles, while their father used his body as a shield. The black bear stared defiantly at the blade, ready to charge it. Only the blue heron had moved out of harm's way.

Bu Zard saw only one option. He had to stop the machine and keep the animals safe. He flew straight into the cab of the giant machine and attacked the operator, flapping his wings in the man's face. Then he returned to stand with his friends.

The man stopped bulldozing long enough to make a call. "Is this Everglades National Park? Well then, come get your animals." His face was red and his lips trembled as he plucked vulture feathers from his work clothes. "This is the last time. Next time we're calling wildlife control to have these troublemakers locked up for trespassing."

A few minutes later, Bu Zard stood on the opposite side of newly placed barricades and watched as the workmen moved the raccoons from in front of the bulldozer.

"I'm not going back to the Everglades, Bu Zard!" the bear insisted. "I've had it with people invading my space. I'm heading north. It's way too crowded down here for me."

"Jason, please." Bu Zard put his wing out to stop the bear. "Jason, wait. I have another idea. You've got to take a stand at some point."

"Bu Zard, the animals did not show up when you tied yourself to the pole at the ranger station to get attention and they are not here now. Face it, they don't care and won't care until it's *their* home that's being run over. No thanks, no more ideas. I'll figure something out on my own."

"But wait," Bu Zard said. "This one is a really good idea."

Apparently, the bear had had enough of Bu Zard's *good ideas*. He ran off into the pine forest before the vulture could say more.

"Peaceful protest, huh? Told you this wouldn't work," said Frieda as she landed beside the vulture.

Bu Zard watched his friend for a minute, while the wheels turned inside his head. "Oh, this isn't over. I've got a plan to stop these developers that will work. We just need more support from the animals. There is no way that we can do this unless we work together."

"I hate to break this to you, Bu Zard, but look around. If the animals did not come to stop this, how will we possibly unite them to do anything?" Frieda asked.

Bu Zard did look around the newly created job site. He watched the giant earthmover roll over the trees, tearing up the ground in front of it and wiping out the homes of so many friends. In fact, Bu Zard's bird's eye view and his habit of "looking around" was what had gotten him to this point. Over the years, he had noticed the changes being made in South Florida. From the air he had watched as new developments pushed in on all sides of Everglades National Park. The animals had to understand what was happening right now beside the Everglades. This development would affect them. They couldn't remain uninvolved forever.

"I don't know how we'll unite them yet. But first, we'll have to convince them that it's for their good. We need to get the support of just one influential animal they trust and believe in."

"Well, that's obviously not us, so what animal do you have in mind?" asked Frieda. "We don't have a lot of *trust* from one species to the next around here. Some of us are predators and some of *us* are prey, you know."

Bu Zard thought for a moment. "Samuel the alligator is who."

"*Frawnk.*" The very thought of disturbing the big alligator caused Frieda to croak, which she immediately followed with a series of clicks and headshaking. "*Tch, tch, tch.*"

"Wait a minute, Frieda," Bu Zard said. "He is old and wise. His reputation for being fair is known throughout the Everglades. We've got to get him on our side. The animals may be afraid of him, but they'll trust what Samuel has to say."

"What *is* he going to say?" asked Frieda.

"That we are going to . . . " Bu Zard's eyes grew large as he told Frieda about the plan he had been putting together for months, a plan that would take the cooperation of many, many animals to work. "That we are going to form the *United Species of Animals*."

The discreet opossum

Nearby, at a safe distance from the giant machine but close enough to watch the vulture's small group, an opossum hunched discreetly behind a pine tree, trying to blend into the underbrush. At one point, he thought the blue heron had looked directly at him, but he stood motionless and, thankfully, the giant machine distracted her. In the end, he was able to hear the animals' conversation. *His employer* would be interested in the vulture's plan even if the other animals were not. The opossum was sure of that.

Chapter 2

You Must Earn Their Trust

Bu Zard hunted Samuel the alligator for the next two weeks through the Everglades, but every lead he followed turned into a dead end.

"I don't think Samuel wants to be found," said Frieda, after a particularly disappointing day of searching. "He's completely disappeared. He must know we're looking for him. Your plan to get his help to form the *United Species of Animals* may need to be tweaked."

"Don't be ridiculous. Why would he hide from us and how would he know we are looking for him anyway? After all, this park is really big."

"Just saying," said Frieda, "it seems strange that we, and especially you with your keen sense of smell and superior vision, have not found him."

"Just keep looking," said Bu Zard. "He's out there."

The vulture had doubts himself about finding Samuel. It should be easy to find the largest alligator in the 'Glades. Most of the animals kept tabs on where the humongous alligator was in order to keep a safe distance from him. Not even the exotic pythons and menacing anacondas that threatened the animals of the Everglades would go near the big alligator. If Samuel was in the area, the animals knew it, but day after day, Bu Zard's search failed. Finally, two weeks and two days after his search began, Bu Zard caught a break.

He was sitting at the top of a buttonwood tree, airing his wings and visualizing the moment in flight when he was at the top of a thermal, using the warm air currents to stay aloft, not flapping his wings, just soaring above the earth and dreaming. This habit of meditating had always gotten him in trouble at VTS (Vulture Technical School). His instructors had no patience for dreaming *or* meditating students even if he happened to be the fastest learner enrolled in school.

He finished his meditation and started to rehearse the speech he had planned for Samuel when Frieda made an abrupt landing on the branch below him.

"A lot of rumors are floating around out there," she said, as soon as she made herself comfortable. "You wouldn't happen to have anything to do with these rumors, would you, Bu Zard?" The great blue heron moved down the branch, cocking her head sideways to watch his reaction.

"For example?" he asked as he shifted his position until he could avoid seeing Frieda's accusing stare.

"For *example*, some of the animals are saying that oil wells are going to be placed in the Everglades."

"That rumor has *been* out there," he said. "What else you got?"

"The Everglades are going to be drained to make way for a larger airport."

"Haven't heard that one," said Bu Zard. "But, hey, wouldn't put it past them. Is that all?"

"Oh, and *ten thousand* houses are going to be built here."

"I never said ten thousand. More like twenty-five hundred."

"I *knew* it," said Frieda as she flew off the branch. She circled the tree and came to land beside him. "You *did* start it. That rumor sounds just like you. Your lies will get you in trouble."

"First of all, Frieda, how do you know it won't be true? Developments are being built on all the borders of the Everglades. Where else can they go? Mark my words, it's only a matter of time till this very tree we're sitting in is pushed down to make way for a home with a view."

"Well, the animals are afraid that houses will be built deep into the park," said Frieda. "My brother's wife, Lucinda, is even talking about moving to the panhandle of Florida."

"Good, they need to be afraid, but moving is not the answer." Bu Zard shuffled around on the limb. "Instead of running away, they should get involved in saving the Everglades from new developments and help get our water cleaned up. Sometimes, the end justifies the means. We've got to light a fire under the animals. Come on, Frieda. You know I've got *all* of our best interests in mind."

"You don't know what will happen in the future and the truth always comes out, Bu Zard. If they find out that you started this rumor, they'll never trust you, even if you do mean well."

Bu Zard thought about what Frieda said. It was important to win the animals' trust, but it was just as important to get them involved in stopping the development that was polluting the water. And he couldn't do it alone. He cocked his head and said, "Don't think about that stuff right now. Let's just concentrate on finding Samuel. We'll worry about the rumors later."

"Oh, my goodness. That rumor business made me forget. I heard from Betty, the wood stork. Samuel is sunning himself down by Mud Lake. She said—"

Before Frieda could squawk or croak, Bu Zard took off, circling high in the sky while using a warm air current to aid his ascent. Once he reached the top of the thermal, he aimed for Mud Lake and started a rapid descent that reached speeds of sixty miles per hour. The vulture made it to the lake in less than five minutes.

Bu Zard spotted Samuel floating under trees in the long canal leading into the lake. He landed on the lowest branch of the closest tree, near enough to talk but still a safe distance from the largest alligator in the Everglades.

After several moments of uncomfortable silence, Bu Zard hissed and clucked a few times to get the attention of the alligator who was clearly ignoring him.

Samuel's response was to open his mouth as wide as he could and then snap it closed. He did this over and over for several minutes, each time holding his long snout open just long enough for Bu Zard to start counting teeth.

"You're missing a few teeth there," he said.

"I'm old," Samuel replied. "Teeth fall out."

Bu Zard watched the alligator's intimidating mouth movement for a few minutes. "*Why* are you doing that?"

"I'm exercising my jaw."

"You *are* old." Then he thought better of criticizing the gator. "But very wise," he added.

Samuel snapped his mouth shut with a bit more ferocity. "I'm old and irritable. What do you want, Bu Zard?" The alligator was not taken in by the vulture's compliment.

Bu Zard didn't get a chance to answer because Frieda, who could not fly as fast as he could, made a noisy landing in the tree several branches above, causing leaves and small twigs to rain down on Bu Zard.

"Thanks for waiting, Bu Zard," she said sarcastically. The blue heron moved back and forth on the limb until she had made herself comfortable. "You know I can't keep up with you when you take off like that. You didn't even let me finish my sentence. Betty, the wood stork, told me that Samuel has been down here for several weeks, probably avoiding you."

Frieda finished her sentence before she noticed Samuel floating in the canal. "Oh! Hi, Samuel. Didn't see you down there. How have you been?"

"Hello, Frieda," said Samuel. "Avoiding was probably a little harsh. It's more like I've been trying to steer clear of drama. I'm getting old."

"Drama, what drama?" asked Bu Zard. "I'm just trying to put together a group to save the Everglades. What drama do you see in that?"

"Using the word 'save' to start with and by a vulture who is shunned by his own species secondly," answered the alligator.

"Not shunned. I have just chosen birds of a different feather to spend my time with, and I don't see how my odd choice of friends relates to my mission," said Bu Zard.

"Hey, I can hear you," said Frieda from the branch above him. A new shower of leaves and twigs rained down on Bu Zard as she shifted her body weight. "And *I* don't see myself as odd."

Samuel smiled, showing his very sharp teeth.

"Yes, Bu Zard, things are happening in the 'Glades," the alligator said. "Our way of life is coming to an end. So many old friends are disappearing. I agree that we must do something. I don't want to sit by and watch as my species and so many others become extinct. I have heard there are plans to build more homes, destroying even more of the Everglades."

Bu Zard shifted on his branch. He should come clean about the rumor he had started, as Frieda had suggested. Or . . . he could wait and see if the false information he had planted helped to motivate the animals.

He decided to proceed carefully with the alligator and move the conversation toward the polluted water. "The animals know we are in trouble, that what is going on outside the park is upsetting the balance inside the park. Development is polluting our water," Bu Zard said, ignoring Frieda and the hissing noises she was making above him. "If I can just get them to trust me, I have a plan."

"Trust, Bu Zard, is an interesting word to use." Samuel rolled in the water to get a better look at the vulture. "You have to prove to the animals that they can trust you and, until you do, you will not get far with any plan."

"Samuel's right, Bu Zard," said Frieda. "They might listen to an old and very wise alligator, but us? It's very doubtful. They're still calling you Buzzard even if you did change your name to Bu Zard. Changing your name has not changed the animals' feelings about you."

Bu Zard's feathers were immediately ruffled and he puffed up with indignation. "*Buzzard* is a nickname. I'm not even related to a buzzard. I'm a vulture, and I may not be the best-looking animal around, but I *do* help keep the 'Glades clean."

Bu Zard knew he was a strange-looking bird. His featherless head was red and much smaller than the rest of his body. He had been teased his whole life for looking like a turkey. As a young vulture, Bu Zard had wanted to be beautiful like the snowy egrets or colorful like the flamingos. He spent days gathering the feathers of these birds, arranging them between his own dingy brown feathers in hopes his new look would brighten his appearance. This had not gone well for him. His family and friends had called him crazy and many had stopped talking to him altogether. Only Frieda understood, and it was with Frieda that Bu Zard had explored and discovered the beauty of the Everglades, a beauty that was now being threatened.

"Your last two plans did not go so well," said Samuel, bringing Bu Zard back to the present. "Tying yourself to the flagpole at the ranger station to impress the tourists was not a good idea. It's a good thing they had that cherry picker available to cut you down. You probably looked pretty silly hanging by your foot."

"You heard about that, did you?" replied Bu Zard, dropping his head a bit at the memory of humiliation. "I was only trying to get the attention of the public. We need their help."

"And you almost got an entire raccoon family run over a few weeks ago at that development site," Samuel added.

Frieda spoke up to support her friend. "To be fair, the bulldozer did stop when Bu Zard flew into the cab."

"Just long enough to move those raccoons," said Samuel. "But, I admire your dedication to the preservation of our homes. It really boils down to the way you go about things. Your plans are not well thought out, which leads to poor execution and ends with bad results."

"But *this* plan will work," Bu Zard assured the alligator. Then, realizing it was time to show his trust in Samuel, he flew from the tree and landed on the ground beside the alligator. "Our water *is* polluted and development *is* closing in on every border of our Everglades National Park. This could be our last stand. Don't you see, Samuel, that some of us are meant to lead? We have to unite the animals."

"Okay, tell me your plan, Bu Zard," said Samuel, "and I will consider it."

The ferns have ears

Not far from the tree that Bu Zard and Frieda had sat in, beneath a clump of ferns with overlaid fronds, a pointy snout appeared, followed by the white and black head of the opossum.

“Okay, tell me your plan, Bu Zard,” said Samuel, “and I will consider it.”

The opossum moved the fronds carefully, not making any sounds that would give away his hiding place. The three animals could not find out he was listening.

The sneaky opossum had been able to find the alligator much faster than Bu Zard, who had searched for weeks. When he had overheard Bu Zard's plan a few weeks earlier to enlist the help of the respected alligator, the opossum used his various contacts to help him find the alligator before Bu Zard could. Next, he found a place to hide that was close to the canal. Then he waited. Finally his patience paid off.

The opossum was in the perfect spot when Samuel's visitors arrived. He heard everything. The opossum concentrated on the conversation as Bu Zard unfolded even more of his plan than he had previously. The sneaky little animal did not move a muscle until Bu Zard and Frieda finished talking to Samuel. Then, when he was sure he would not be seen, he moved quickly from beneath the ferns, scurrying through the palmettos and around the small palms that stood in his way, his skinny, hairless tail waving behind him. He had to get this information to his boss right away.

Chapter 3

Half-Moon Means Trouble

A few days after Bu Zard's meeting with Samuel, on a moonless night, a lone truck crept along one of the many roads crisscrossing the Everglades. A high-powered beam, aimed at the side of the road, flashed from the roof of the truck. The light, which was controlled from inside the cab, moved in and out of the roadside foliage, illuminating trees, undergrowth, electric poles, and the trash that littered the ditches.

A man hunched over the steering wheel of the old pickup. Swarms of insects found the truck's high beams inviting and blocked his view. The man squinted in an attempt to see past the bugs as they dive-bombed the windshield.

The only light inside the truck came from the instrument panel on the dashboard. It cast a dim glow on the man who had attempted to disguise himself by pulling a large hat down over his ears and wearing dark sunglasses. Since there was no sun or moon, this would seem strange to anyone who met the man, but it was past midnight so very few people were out and about in this part of the Everglades. Everything else about the man was hidden in the darkness of the truck and by his disguise, except for his necktie, which was imprinted with tiny yellow half-moons.

A very big boar sat on the front seat next to the man. Two large tusks protruded from his massive jaw below his two tiny piggy eyes. The boar's body filled the entire passenger side of the truck, making it difficult for the man to see around him. The boar, fighting to stay awake, was losing his battle and let his head slump against the window.

The man was not paying attention to the boar as he drove along in silence, watching the road ahead. Only when the spotlight suddenly shot up into the tops of the trees did the man realize his passenger was dozing.

"Ollie, wake up!" said the man. "Pay attention! Do you see him? He told me he would be between mile marker seventy-five and seventy-six. We can't drive around all night waiting for him to show up."

"Sorry, boss." The boar moved the light to illuminate objects farther back from the road. "Nope," he said after sweeping the powerful beam back and forth over the area for the second time. "There's nothing out there but weeds, trash, and a dead opossum a couple hundred feet back."

The man stomped on the brake pedal.

The boar, who had been unable to get the seat belt around his large body, slammed against the dash, lodging his tusks into the front of the glove compartment.

"Are you dense? He's not dead. He's faking. Cut the light and wait here," the man said. "I'll be back in a minute."

"*Ooooooeeeeeee*," Ollie squealed through clenched teeth as he pulled back on his tusks. Grunting and pulling with all his might, the boar flew back into the seat when his tusks came out of the dash.

Ollie leaned over to watch the man through the truck's side mirror, but all he could see was the beam of the flashlight moving up and down the roadway, so the boar sat back in his seat and waited.

The man walked along the road, looking for the opossum. Gravel crunched under his feet, and he had to lean away several times when the rough sawgrass, growing in water-filled ditches, scratched against his skin. Cicadas, frogs, and crickets, accompanied by a lone bullfrog with a slightly off-key croak, kept a constant rhythm with his steps. The man hurried. Though the Everglades may be deserted of people at this time of night, it crawled with life. His appearance here would not go unnoticed.

Bzzzzzz, bzzzzzz. The mosquitoes, sensing his presence, rapidly moved in and circled his head. The man swatted at the annoying insects while shining his flashlight up and down the ditches. Finally, he spotted the outline of a partially hidden opossum lying beside a palmetto bush. He walked over to the animal, put his boot against its fur, and shook it back and forth.

"Hey, is that you, T.J.?" asked the man while knowing full well it was T.J.

The man had recruited the animal to gather information. T.J. was a natural at sensing potential trouble in areas the company wanted to move into and good at negotiating a deal with troublemakers opposing the company's plans. T.J., a highly compensated employee, was moving up the ranks fast within the company.

"Of course it's me," whispered the opossum. "We need to be quick. I can't be seen meeting you."

"You're the one who called me." The man slapped his neck and swatted at the fat mosquito biting him. "What's so important that I had to drive into the Everglades in the middle of the night?"

"The animals are up to something big," said the opossum. "Somehow they found out about our plans to build deep into the Everglades."

"How could that happen? We've been very careful to keep that a secret," said the man. "Who would have told them?" Both the man and the opossum turned and looked at the truck where the boar waited.

"Nah," said the man. "Ollie's too lazy. They must have found out some other way."

"Well," said the opossum. "It doesn't matter how they found out. It's not as important as this news. These animals have a plan to stop everything we're working toward. This is definitely big trouble for you and your bosses. *And* there is talk of involving the Governor!"

"What kind of plan could they possibly come up with? I need details. When did this happen? Where? Who's involved? What else can you tell me?" asked the man.

"A small group met last week in the Everglades. The crazy turkey vulture—the one who's been giving us all that trouble on our work sites—was there. He has some powerful backup this time."

"What? That's ludicrous," said the man. "They're just animals living in some mosquito-infested, low-lying, mudhole. People don't care what's happening down here. Go back and try to stop them."

"How am I going to do that? You told me to get in touch with you if I sensed trouble brewing in the Everglades. Well, I do. You knew they would not be quiet forever. The animals are worried about their homes."

"All right, all right! Stay close to them. Let me know *everything* you find out. Immediately!" the man ordered the opossum. "The animals cannot be allowed to interfere with our plans; too much time and money has already been invested and we definitely can't afford to have the politicians involved any more than they already are."

"What are we going to do boss?" the opossum asked. "How are we going to stop the animals from interfering?"

The man stared at the opossum until the animal took an involuntary step back. "Just do your job and stay with them. We hired you to spy on the animals, so spy on them. Get close to the leaders. And I guess we'll have to start the relocation process sooner than planned," he said.

"But the facility's not ready."

"You let me worry about the relocation facility. You worry about the animals. Are we clear?"

The man turned abruptly and started toward his truck, flashing his light as he walked. The beam of the flashlight caught the side of the vehicle and illuminated the writing on the door. HM CONSOLIDATED ENTERPRISES stood out in bold black letters. A yellow half-moon was stamped above the words. The man grabbed the handle and jerked his door open.

"Be careful and don't get caught," he said before climbing into the truck and driving away.

T.J. watched the truck until he could no longer see its taillights. Then he headed back into the thick underbrush of the Everglades.

Chapter 4

The Birds Are the First to Arrive

Bu Zard stood on the stump of a red mangrove and watched as Frieda paced uncomfortably along the shoreline of the Everglades' mangrove forest.

The tall bird with soft, blue-gray plumage looked around nervously. Her eyes darted first to the sky and then to the water. She jerked around and stared intensely into the dense mangroves that partially surrounded the tree island. "*Tch, tch, tch,*" she croaked.

"Frieda, relax," the turkey vulture said from behind her, catching the jittery blue heron off guard. Frieda took off in flight, circling the mangroves several times before coming back to land beside Bu Zard.

Today, they would try to unite the animals. Bu Zard's ambitious plan would require the cooperation of a majority of the animals living in Everglades National Park.

"This is not a good idea, Bu Zard," Frieda said. "This is dangerous, and it's stupid. Some of these animals coming to meet us have sharp teeth, you know. How did I let you talk me into this?"

"Because, we need all the species represented, Frieda. The harmless ones and the dangerous ones. We want total agreement among us all. Don't worry so much, just trust me." Bu Zard turned his head to look in the various directions that Frieda had been nervously watching moments before. "They're coming from all over the Everglades because they want to help. The truce among the species will hold."

Bu Zard had worked hard putting this meeting together and it had not been easy. Samuel had only agreed to help Bu Zard if they could find four other influential animals to go along with the plan. This had been harder than the vulture thought it would be.

The panthers, who commanded as much respect as Samuel the alligator, refused to get involved. They were "disinclined to be involved, even remotely, with humans," preferring instead to stay hidden deep in the Everglades.

Luckily, the bald eagles were more receptive, especially when Bu Zard told them Samuel was *definitely* involved. Just a small white lie and something Bu Zard hoped would soon become true.

He convinced Victor, a powerful deer that couldn't attend the meeting, to send his family to represent him.

Finally, Bu Zard had contacted the animal entertainment industry. He needed a celebrity (of a sort) to validate the march. The vulture was hoping that the name recognition of a rich and famous animal would convince the media and public that their cause was real.

Now, here he stood in Anhinga Bay on an ancient coral and limestone beach, trying to keep the peace.

Bu Zard took a deep breath of the salty bay air, mixed with decaying leaves and rotting wood from the island, and exhaled slowly. Time to put the plan in motion; he would just have to keep his wings crossed that the animals would be supportive.

The birds had been the first to arrive that morning, the owls before dawn, followed by the waders and the small shore birds.

It was a little before noon and almost all the birds were here; a great number of species were represented. Red-throated loons, cormorants, and anhinga that had fished all morning now dried their wings atop every available branch on the island. Herons, egrets, and a few wood storks waded in the shallow water searching for small shrimp, crab, and minnows, while sandpipers followed behind, running back and forth in a wave of white and gray.

Since early morning, it had been chaos and, instead of organizing as planned, Frieda stood in knee-deep water, helping a quacking mother duck search for her lost ducklings.

The smaller birds were tucked and hidden inside the tangled web of red mangroves growing out of the tea-colored water, while purple gallinule, along with the more common bluebirds, blue jays, doves, pigeons, and crows, crowded onto the outer mangrove branches. The noises from the variety of birds with their associated caws, coos, and whistles were deafening.

Bu Zard reached for the large, red whistle that hung, unnoticed, around his neck until he began to blow into it and an ear-piercing shrill filled the air.

"Birds, birds, can you listen up? Please, listen!" he bellowed. Bu Zard opened his wings to a full span and blew on the whistle until all was quiet. "There is plenty of room, plenty of room. We have several hours before all the animals invited will arrive. Spread out if you need more space. Frieda here," and with that Bu Zard pointed the tip of his very large wing to his assistant, "Frieda will help you find your species or," and here he paused and shook his head in exasperation as a gaggle of goslings raced under his outstretched wings, "or your family. Birds, please keep your children under control. Frieda! Frieda, help me out here."

Frieda waded through the round-stemmed spike rush grass, dragging a list of names through the water. "The yellow-bellied sapsuckers refuse to sit with the rest of the woodpeckers," she stammered. "And you promised I would have help with the species chart."

Frieda was prepared to go on and on about all of the problems she was sure she would encounter, but pandemonium broke out among the birds.

All eyes and beaks turned to the sky. The birds of prey had arrived.

From the north came the hawks and falcons spiraling downward into a tighter and tighter loop until they rolled into a gravity-defying dive, pulling up inches above the treetops. One after another, they made their entrance and came to rest in the coco plum and buttonwood trees covering the island directly behind the mangroves.

The ospreys and the kites came next. While their entrance was not as threatening, their size was intimidating, and unrest among the smaller birds became an issue. The wrens and swallows threatened to leave.

The relative peace of the morning was replaced with a feeling of apprehension. Bu Zard moved from group to group, trying to reassure each about the truce that had been worked out.

"You have nothing to worry about," he told a ruby-throated hummingbird that buzzed by his head several times, agitated by the larger birds. "*All* the birds are part of the truce."

Finally, in exasperation, he raised his wings and once again blew his whistle. Three short bursts this time. Then he turned and looked across the small bay at two large birds perched on a backcountry chickee, a wooden, elevated platform used by hikers spending the night in the Everglades.

The birds spread their wings and flew from the chickee. They were above the treetops in seconds.

Bu Zard watched as his backups, two very respected and influential animals, approached.

With their unmistakable white heads and white tail feathers, the two enormous birds soared high above the tree island. The pair of Southern bald eagles had agreed to help Bu Zard keep peace at the meeting. The other birds immediately settled down.

Chapter 5

The Problem with Crocs

"There just is not enough space for this right now," Bu Zard told a young mallard duck arguing with a Canada goose over fishing rights in the small bay. "I need you to work with me. Just work with me."

He turned away from the two and headed toward Frieda. The mid-afternoon sun put a glare, as well as a sparkle, on the bay's brackish water. The reflection flashed into Bu Zard's eyes, temporarily blinding him. He raised one large wing over his head for shade just in time to see three enormous crocodiles bearing down on Frieda.

Frieda stood in shallow water, checking names off her species chart. "Roseate spoonbills, check. Great snowy egrets, check." She paused. Tiny ripples of water lapped at her feet. The feathers on her long, gray neck stood up while goosebumps ran down her skinny legs.

"Frieda!" Bu Zard called. "Watch—" But it was too late. The crocodiles lunged from the water and circled the blue heron on their hind legs.

"*Squawk*," Frieda screeched and looked wildly around for help. "Bu Zard!"

The three crocodiles locked their front legs. "Harrumph, harrumph, harrumph," they began to sing. "Swimming, swimming over the deep blue sea. Do the funky chicken's dance and we shall set you free!" The three danced in a circle around the startled heron.

"Stop, stop!" Bu Zard flew from the shore at the three crocodiles, blowing his bright red whistle. But Frieda had already dropped her lists and organizational charts into the water and taken flight, her long legs slanted out behind her.

The Croc Brothers (as the three American crocodiles were known in the Everglades) continued to dance and laugh while Frieda flew in circles around the marsh. The bald eagles flew in to talk the wading bird down. It took several more turns above the treetops before she was convinced that the jokesters below were truly harmless.

Finally, Frieda calmed her nerves enough to come down. She landed beside Bu Zard and shook her head in disgust, backing slowly away from the Croc Brothers.

"Dancing crocodiles, Bu Zard? Really?" Frieda questioned her friend when she had composed herself enough to talk.

"Boys, come on. You're supposed to be helping me with the walk, not creating more problems," Bu Zard told the crocodiles, as he stood between them and Frieda. "We have rules for this meeting that you agreed to, one of which was orderly conduct."

Larry, the older brother, waved at the obviously flustered great blue heron. "*Ahhhh*, we weren't trying to hurt you, girlie. You know it was all in good fun. Look," he said, pointing. "Look what we've brought to you."

Frieda was leery about taking her eyes off the brothers, but, out of curiosity, took a hesitant glance in the direction Larry was pointing. The water was moving. Frieda's beak dropped open as she stared at the open area of the bay.

"Reptiles are what you wanted. Reptiles are what we brought," Larry said, then giggled as he and his two brothers began their dance once again. "Harrumph, harrumph, harrumph, swimming, swimming across the deep blue bay, reptiles, reptiles have come with us to play."

The Croc Brothers danced a few more steps. Then they slipped, one-by-one, into the water. A few moments later, they surfaced, doing a synchronized backstroke, until they were among the incoming wave of reptilian cousins. With a great deal of fanfare, they led the group to shore.

"Very good, very good, boys. You've done a wonderful job," cried Bu Zard as he danced in excitement. "Look, Frieda. Alligators, turtles, crocodiles, and snakes! We have snakes. Yes, this is good, all good. Do you see that? They have—I believe they have a hawksbill turtle with them, and is that a Kemp's ridley? Oh this is wonderful! Just wonderful!"

In addition to the saltwater turtles, freshwater turtles had made the trip too, swimming through the brackish mix of salt and fresh water to attend the meeting.

For the first time since the early morning arrivals, Bu Zard felt confident with his plan. He immediately began coordinating his newest guests. As he looked around at the number of animals that had already arrived, he relaxed for the first time that day. "Frieda, we want to keep all animals with their species. We need to keep things as organized as possible."

"I'm not coordinating the snakes, Bu Zard, or the alligators. I can handle the turtles, but I'm drawing the line on the rest of that group," Frieda said under her breath.

She bent her head down and started searching for the lists she had been working with before the arrival of the Croc Brothers. Finally, she found them and pulled them from the bay, dripping, but readable. "Okay, we have green turtles, striped mud turtles, peninsula cooters, soft-shell, and Florida red-bellies. All of the freshwater turtles follow me." Frieda turned and walked rapidly through the water along the edge of the mangrove forest toward a spot where a log jam of fallen trees created the perfect place for the turtles to sit. She tried to ignore the water snakes that were now reaching the shore in large numbers and walked away from the area as quickly as she could, forgetting the fact that *turtles* were following her.

Bu Zard threw his wings up in the air and turned back to face the Croc Brothers, congratulating them for the large number of reptiles they had brought to the meeting and missing the detail that Frieda had left a few of the turtles behind.

You're not a bird

"Wow," said the smallest soft-shell turtle. She had fallen *way* behind the other turtles. The little turtle left the water and walked up onto the limestone beach. She had promised her mother to follow the rules and stay with her aunt, but all too quickly, she became caught up in the excitement of the meeting and lost sight of her relatives.

"Wow, look at all the birds," she said, spinning in circles, trying to get a better view of the mangroves and hardwood trees on the island. In her excitement, the turtle bumped into a bright red tree.

"Watch it," hissed a voice from the branches of the gumbo-limbo tree.

"Hey, who's there?" asked the turtle. She stopped and peered into the branches. "Hey there, I'm Desta. Who are you?" Desta pushed herself over a root of the red tree to get a better look.

"You should be with your friends," said the voice from the tree. This is not a good place for unsupervised baby turtles."

Desta looked up into the center of the tree. She could see a furry creature hiding behind the many branches of the gumbo-limbo. The funny-looking animal with the white and black face had a long snout and was perched on a branch with his long, hairless tail wrapped around it to hold him steady.

"I'm not a baby and you're not a bird," said Desta. "Who are you?"

"Are you blind? What do I look like? I'm an opossum," he hissed. "Now go away and stop bothering me."

"You . . . " Desta paused and stretched her neck out of her shell to get a really good look at the opossum. Then with confidence, she said, "*You* are a mammal. I learned that in turtle school. The mammals are not supposed to be here yet. It was in the directions we were given. Birds were to arrive first, next amphibians and reptiles, than the mammals. Why are you here so early?"

"Are you blind? What do I look like?
I'm an opossum," he hissed.

"I'm a marsupial, nosey," replied the opossum. "There were no rules for marsupials."

"It doesn't matter what kind of soup you are. Mammals are *not* supposed to be here yet," Desta argued with the opossum.

"*Hiss*, go away, you annoying turtle." The opossum turned away from Desta.

A foul-smelling odor filtered down from the tree. That was enough for her. Desta crawled away as quickly as her short legs could take her. She needed to find the others. She needed to stay with her species, she thought, as she hurried away from the opossum to find her aunt.

It will all be explained

An organized kind of chaos took over the afternoon. The animals stayed with their species but remained on edge and nervous, mostly because of their natural instincts to stay far away from any threat. Frieda and Bu Zard worked tirelessly, answering questions and keeping the animals calm. "It will all be explained when we start the meeting," they said patiently over and over again. "It will all be explained soon."

As the afternoon sun disappeared into the western horizon, a family of red foxes appeared at the water's edge. A raccoon sauntered in, followed closely by a bobcat. Three white-tailed deer, a mother and two babies, arrived from one side of the tree island at the same time a mother bear and two cubs darted in from the other side. Otters, minks, and moles skittered between the feet of the larger animals and, on several occasions, tripped a few. The rats and a few marsh rabbits ran out of the bay after swimming from a neighboring island. It seemed as if an unheard signal had been sent throughout the Everglades. The mammals, for the most part, all arrived together.

Chapter 6
A Case of Nerves

"Order, order everyone." Bu Zard had been yelling and blowing his whistle for almost ten minutes, but nothing worked to calm the nerves of all the animals now present. Since the arrival of the mammals, the tree island and half of the bay were in total turmoil. "Quiet!" Bu Zard shouted. He looked around for Frieda.

He found her stalking back and forth in the shallow water, muttering to herself and shaking her head. "*Tch, tch, tch*, I knew this wouldn't work, just knew it. I asked Bu Zard, 'Bu Zard, who's going to listen to us? Why would any of the animals believe what we have to say?' 'Don't worry,' you said." Frieda paused in the middle of her tirade and looked like she was going to fly away. "Don't worry! Is he kidding?"

Even Bu Zard was beginning to worry. Yes, with a little help from his rumor, the animals had finally acknowledged they needed to do something. They had unanimously agreed that their homes in the Everglades were in trouble and they needed to talk about it. But these were all natural enemies sitting side-by-side. There was only so much control that he could have over this group. After all, he *was* only a turkey vulture and not a very popular one at that. He turned his attention back to the disorder around him and shook his head. *Maybe I should rethink my escape plan.*

A turtle's new friends

Desta found a place on an old log. She wiggled into the smallest space she could find at the end of a long line of turtles. The little turtle could not decide whether to keep her head in her shell for protection or stick her head out to watch all the excitement happening on every side.

She watched as a large reptile head surfaced in the center of the bay and moved toward the tree island. Its eyes glowed red in the early evening light, its attention focused on the animals along the shore.

Around her, rows of turtles lined up on logs that were half buried in the muddy bottom of the bay. Nearby, a mother deer watched over her children.

A commotion caught Desta's attention. She turned in time to see a mother bear, followed by her two cubs, push her way closer to the edge of the water. "Who's in charge?" the bear asked, as she ran up and down the water's edge.

The doe took her eyes off of her children to watch the anxious bear.

"I need to speak to someone in charge," the bear said to no one in particular. Then she caught sight of the doe. "You there, can you help me? This is important. It's about my son, Jason. I must speak to the organizer."

"No, I'm sorry. I don't know. Maybe check with the red-headed vulture, Bu Zard, over there with the raccoons. He seems to be telling all the animals where to go," the doe spoke softly to the anxious bear.

While the mother deer's attention was on the bear, the two fawns edged closer and closer to the log Desta sat on. The turtle pulled her head inside her shell.

"Tony, stop! Where are you going?" asked the female fawn. "Mother told us to stay by her."

"*Shhh*, Sophie. I'm only looking at the turtles. There must be a thousand of them," Tony said to his sister, and then he put his nose down close to Desta's head.

Desta pulled herself as far inside her shell as she could and hoped the deer would go away.

"Hey, anybody in there?" the deer yelled into Desta's seemingly empty shell. Desta poked her head out of her shell.

"Stop yelling! I'm not deaf. I'm Desta, and I'm not supposed to talk to you," she told Tony. She tried to turn her body so she wouldn't have to look at the nosey deer. "Mom said stay with your species. Those are the rules for everyone, you know."

Sophie interrupted. "Tony, get over here. The meeting is about to start."

The deer ignored his sister and continued talking to Desta. "I know the rules, but what's the point? It's a meeting to help *all* of us, isn't it?"

"The *point* is to keep us from eating each other," Desta said, looking back over her shell.

"I guess that's a good point," said Tony.

Desta pulled her head back into her shell and tried to edge farther away from Tony. In doing so, she moved a bit too much and fell off the log.

She heard the deer's snort while she was splashing around in the water.

"Sorry," the deer told her. "I didn't mean to laugh at you."

Sophie jumped side to side and pawed at the sand back on the beach, trying to get her brother's attention.

Desta wished the deer would listen to his sister instead of watching her as she struggled to get back to her place on the log. But, unfortunately, by the time Desta returned, her spot had been taken by another turtle.

"Hey, Desta, come stand with Sophie and me," Tony whispered to the turtle. "*We* won't bite. It will be an adventure. Come on. I'm Tony and that's my sister Sophie."

Desta looked around, hoping for another option, but seeing none, sighed and said, "Okay, but I'm not going far from the water." Then, glancing around to see if any turtles were watching her, she followed the deer to their place beside the water's edge.

Tony leaned down and whispered, "They're starting the meeting."

Bu Zard had given up on total order and was beginning his speech.

In a very sincere voice, he addressed the animals. "For those who don't know me, my name is Bu Zard, and we are here today to discuss a very serious life-altering threat to all of the species here and around our state. We are living in a time of grave—"

"Get to the point," a voice yelled from somewhere high in a tree.

"This better be good," said a duck surrounded by her ducklings. "Putting us all in this kind of danger, it just better be good."

The voice from the gumbo-limbo tree boomed out again. "There is no problem. We've been brought here to help the career of this turkey buzzard."

Bu Zard jerked at the less-than-friendly use of the nickname he had tried to get rid of.

The noise level from the animals began to increase.

Desta tapped on Tony's foot to get his attention. "I know that voice. It's coming from the red tree over there. It's a marsoup, or something like that."

Tony and Desta were both leaning forward to see if they could spot the heckler but, instead, saw an enormous reptile moving rapidly toward the vulture.

The approaching alligator let out a bellow. It was a familiar sound to the animals of the Everglades. The American alligator came to where Bu Zard was standing. He bellowed again, showing his fierceness and authority over the bay. The alligator was at least fifteen feet long.

"That's Samuel," said Tony. Then he gave Desta her second piece of advice for the day. "Stay away from him. Mom says he's always in a bad mood, and you'll know what mood he's in by how fast his tail is moving back and forth. The faster his tail moves, the madder he is."

Desta nodded. Then she turned her attention back to Bu Zard.

"Samuel, thank goodness you've arrived," said Bu Zard to the alligator. "I was just starting the meeting."

"I've been here, Bu Zard," said Samuel, whipping his tail across the water and causing a small wave to hit the shore. "*All day*."

Desta backed up, putting distance between herself and the alligator. Tony stayed right beside her.

"Just to be on the safe side, we better give him some room," she whispered to her new friend.

Chapter 7
Desperate Times Call for Desperate Actions

Bu Zard turned to the animals and raised his wings in a grand gesture. "Animals, here to speak to—"

"We are here," Samuel interrupted, "each of you are here because you know there is a problem. The continuing development around the Everglades is affecting us. And now we are faced with a water crisis that could be the final blow to many of our species. There has already been a two hundred percent decline in the number of species of birds found in the Everglades. Animals are disappearing at an alarming rate. We could not find some of the animals that only a few years ago were here in large numbers. We are running out of space, and now there is talk of new development moving deep into the Everglades."

Bu Zard grimaced, but only Frieda noticed.

Samuel paused in his speech, giving the animals an opportunity to voice their opinions. But instead, for the first time that day, all the animals were silent. Only the sound of a far off airboat could be heard humming through the Everglades. The alligator continued, "The neighborhoods and farms keep taking up more and more of our space and endangering the water as well as our native animals. Our water flows over hundreds of miles of developed land to get to us. What is not diverted through canals and into man-made basins is carrying harmful chemicals by the time it arrives in the Everglades."

"How long do you think we have before it is too late to save our homes?" asked a pileated woodpecker.

"Is it even possible to save them?" asked an old gopher tortoise that had just arrived from the other side of the tree island. "I've moved seven times in the last four years to make way for new developments. Two of those times, I was actually forcefully picked up and moved. I'm just too tired to keep doing this," he told the crowd.

"Have you ever heard of relocating out of state?" shouted the voice from the trees. "Maybe to the mountains or the Southwest?"

Bu Zard looked around for the animal that was interrupting.

"We can't do this alone. We need help from the people of the state. More than that, we need help from the people of this country," continued Samuel, ignoring the heckler. "Our problem is their problem. Our water is their water. If the water is harmful to us, it is harmful to them. If it makes us sick to live in it and drink it, it will also make humans sick when they play in it or drink it. Chemicals, not disposed of properly, pollute the fresh water in lakes and streams. And we cannot allow any more intrusion into the Everglades."

"So what do you expect us to do?" asked the voice from the tree. "We're only animals. We can't do anything. This is a national park. Let the government take care of it. Every animal should just go home and take care of themselves. *Protect your own!*"

This created a new outburst from the animals. The mother duck began gathering her ducklings under her wings and moving them out into the bay. Animals all over the tree island began to round up their offspring, pushing them together in a hurry to get away and back to the safety of their homes.

Samuel let out a bellow that thundered through the 'Glades, piercing the night with its ferocity and silencing the animals. The animals froze, some in fear of the great alligator, others wondering what Samuel would do to the voice of opposition.

Samuel did the unexpected. He lowered his voice and continued his speech, ignoring the negative remarks. "Listen to us," he said. "We have a plan. Leave if you want, but these problems will only get worse. You cannot hide. We have a plan and it will take all of us to make it work. I have lived in the Everglades many years, and I have witnessed the changes. For our children and then their children, you must stay and listen."

Bu Zard held his breath. The next few minutes would be crucial. The majority of the animals had to be onboard for the plan to work.

The doe took a bold step forward, nudging her two startled offspring out of the way. "We are listening, Samuel, and we will support your plan," she said, determination in her voice. "We have had many family members and friends affected by bad water and the plants clogging the waterways. Victor, my mate, will be joining us and he has asked me to tell you that we will support you in any way we can."

"Thank you, Wanda," responded Samuel. "And please let Victor know that his support is also greatly appreciated."

The bald eagles flew in and landed on an old mangrove stump. "Count on us," said the male eagle named Benson. "Our species was almost wiped out once before, in my father's lifetime, because of pollution to our water and food supply. We cannot let it happen again. We will keep order, as well as help with the plan."

"Tell us," called a young bobcat that had moved closer to the front. "Tell us the plan. We are not leaving. I have traveled to many places, and I can tell you that humans do not think about us. What can we do to change this?"

Bu Zard let out the breath he was holding and stepped forward. But before he could speak, a group of turkey vultures and black vultures hissed at him, causing a break in the momentum of the meeting.

"Let Samuel talk, buzzard. We did not come here to listen to you."

"*Tch, tch, tch.* Don't pay attention, Bu Zard," Frieda told him. "Tell them, just like you rehearsed."

So, in his usual grandiose style, Bu Zard waved his wings as he unfolded the plan.

"We march," he said. "Or walk, crawl, fly, however you prefer. We march, right through the middle of the state. We must unite and take our problems to the people and to the doorstep of the Governor himself."

The Croc Brothers began their silly dance again, accompanied by a new song. "Marching, marching, we are marching to the cap-*ee*-tol."

"Whoa, whoa, whoa," said the invisible heckler. "You are asking us to expose ourselves, make ourselves vulnerable to every danger out there. We can't even trust each other, much less the people. This is too chancy and not worth risking our lives. I'm going home."

This comment sent another roar up from the crowd. All of the animals were trying to speak at once. The hisses coming from the group of vultures added to the level of disorder.

Bu Zard was annoyed. The unseen heckler was messing up his speech, and the plan depended on the majority of the animals agreeing. Bu Zard looked to Samuel for help. "Need some crowd control here. Step in anytime," he said out of the side of his beak.

Samuel roared. "Who are you? Show yourself and come forward. Then we will address your concerns."

There was no answer or movement from the gumbo-limbo tree.

Bu Zard turned to the crowd once more. "We have taken measures to insure the safety of the animals. We have arranged a truce. We have guardians who will be with us at all times. Benson, the eagle, will watch from the sky. Samuel will protect from the ground. I've arranged TV coverage all along the route. We've even sent messages to the Governor. The representatives in the state legislature will be meeting to discuss new laws and budgets."

"Wait! Stop!" The opossum lowered himself out of the tree, giving the crowd their first glimpse of the opposition to the plan. "Legislature and representatives? What is all this you talk about? What do we know about legislators, and how is it you know so much, turkey buzzard?" he asked. "When did you become such an expert on our government?"

Desta, who had been listening intently to the vulture and alligator, tapped Tony's foot and whispered, "See, I told you it was the marsoup."

"He's an opossum," Tony whispered back.

Bu Zard turned and pointed his wing toward two brown pelicans sitting atop channel markers. "They told me," he said.

The pelicans, who had seemed unconcerned with the meeting only moments before, flew from their perch toward the crowd. They landed in the water and floated as close to Bu Zard as they could get before speaking to the animals.

"We have spent many years around people, long enough to understand that representatives in the legislature make the laws and budgets for the state," said the first pelican. "Yes, we told Bu Zard. We know everything. We spend hours floating by their boats, eating the fish they throw to us. We sit outside the restaurants and along the piers and we listen. We know when the politicians meet, what their plans are, when they are in town and when they are not." The pelican paused to let his friend talk.

"The lawmakers are meeting at the end of the month to discuss the natural resources of the state. We've heard they will discuss a new law that will stop the development that is destroying animal habitats outside Everglades National Park. It will also have provisions to clean up the water flowing into the park. There are many who are for this law."

"And there are many against it," finished the first pelican. "We must get there *before* they vote. It is the way to influence change."

"This is our chance," Bu Zard interrupted. "We draw attention to our problem with the march, and we finish on the steps of the Capitol of Florida. With all the publicity, we cannot be ignored." The turkey vulture finished his argument with his wings raised and a glare aimed at the opossum. "Desperate times call for desperate actions. If we leave by the end of next week, we will arrive in Tallahassee in time to meet with the elected officials. They are responsible for approving the 'Save the Everglades' bill. We have a chance to influence change together! The *United Species of Animals*! Together we are strong!"

As he waited for a response from the animals, Bu Zard caught a movement out of the corner of his eye and turned in time to watch an enormous turtle with a large, wide head, a prominent pink spot on top of his skull, and a shell at least seven feet long crawl from the water. The turtle used his flippers to push himself across the sand, coming to rest in front of Bu Zard.

A leatherback, thought Bu Zard, as he smiled at the animal before addressing him. "Welcome, welcome. I'm glad you could join us today," said Bu Zard.

The big turtle used his flippers to move sand around as he made himself comfortable.

Some of it flew through the air, landing on the other animals, but none moved or said a word. They seemed to be in awe of the giant turtle.

"I am from the Caribbean, Mon," said the turtle, his accent thick with a melody heard most often in the islands. "I have come to tell my brothers and sisters that this idea to unite is important. This water that flows across your land and into the waters throughout the Everglades also flows far into the Caribbean. We are all affected. My brother and sister fishes, they come to these waters south of here to spawn their young. My family travels from faraway shores to build nests and lay their eggs. We ask that you take our message with you. We are all endangered when the waters are polluted."

"Come with us," said Bu Zard. "You can tell your story to the Governor."

"That is impossible," said the turtle. "I would not be able to make that journey. It would be much too difficult for me. I am asking my cousin turtles to support you, to go with you on this trip and represent those of us not suited for the land."

The giant leatherback turtle shuffled sand around and began crawling back toward the bay. Seven ridges ran down its long, rubbery shell, coming together at the very back and ending in a point. The turtle's head was the last thing Bu Zard could see of the leatherback as it swam into the bay then dropped beneath the surface.

The animals had stood in silence as they listened to the turtle. Now, somewhere from the back of the crowd, a chant started. Soon all of the animals joined in. "USA, USA. Save our 'Glades. Save our water. USA, USA." The animals rushed forward, crowding around and trying to talk to Bu Zard and Samuel. The Croc Brothers did a dance, and the opossum slipped quietly away.

Desta looked up at the deer standing beside her. She had never heard anything like this, not in turtle school or anywhere else.

"That turtle was cool," she finally said to Tony.

"Totally awesome relative you got there," said Tony. "We're going. Are you in? This will be a big adventure. The chance of a lifetime. You can walk with us."

The little turtle squirmed inside her shell. "Su-su-sure," she stuttered. She did not know if she wanted to go on the march to Tallahassee. She'd never been out of the Everglades. She certainly couldn't go with the deer family. But the leatherback's words had been important. She, just a little turtle, was needed to carry a message. Saving the Everglades was important for many animals, not just the ones living inside the park's borders. She had to go to the Capitol. She had to represent turtles everywhere.

"I'm going, but I've got to stay with my species," she reminded herself as she made her decision and crawled away.

Chapter 8
Sticking to the Mission

The day for the Animal March arrived quickly. The animals were told they had two weeks to get to the Capitol to make an impression on the elected officials and beg for a vote to protect the Everglades. Bu Zard was not one hundred percent sure how much time they actually did have to get to Tallahassee. He had to depend on the information the pelicans gave him. He hoped to arrive at the Capitol right before the introduction of the "Save the Everglades" bill. Timing would be everything. If they got there too late, the Animal March would be for nothing.

The weather was perfect. The early morning spring fog had already lifted, and the smoke of a distant fire on the tree island was staying far to the south, leaving the sky clear and blue.

Bu Zard stood on a dirt road beside an asphalt highway. He had scheduled the start of the big march for eight thirty in the morning, but at seven fifteen he was not having much luck getting the animals to organize themselves. At the moment, a mother bear with two small cubs blocked the vulture's every move.

"Please, Bu Zard, you *are* our only hope," pleaded the black bear.

Bu Zard paused in the middle of his mission to answer the bear. "Elda, really, we don't have time to stop in the city. Jason's a smart bear. He'll be fine."

The vulture had no idea if Jason would be fine or not. He had not seen the bear since their attempt to stop developers from cutting down the pine forest. There had been stories of a rogue bear tearing into houses around the state, but Bu Zard had not had time to consider the source of the stories. He had been planning the march.

"You're not listening, Bu Zard. He's been picked up twice by the wildlife control officers for breaking and entering," said the mother bear. "They have a three strikes rule. If he's caught—*again*—I shudder to think what will happen to him. If we take the march into Ocala, he can join us. He can blend into the crowd and we can get him out."

Bu Zard laid a large wing on Elda's shoulder. "Elda, you said yourself that he's running wild. We can't risk getting involved with Jason's problems. We have a mission. We must stick to the plan. The plan, the mission, these are the important parts of this entire march."

"Oh, good grief, Bu Zard, how can you spout off like that?" asked Frieda, who had landed behind the vulture in time to hear the end of his speech. "If we are sticking to the mission, then why, pray tell me, did you bring in the pink flamingos?"

"*Ahh*, the flamingos! The divas have at last arrived," Bu Zard said, using Frieda's entrance to distance himself from the mother bear. He turned to face Frieda and clasped his wings together, pleased with the news. "Marketing, my dear. They are influential animals who will lead us on the walk. Four gorgeous birds from Miami—stars, famous beauties. Imagine the attention they will get on and off camera."

"I don't think that the flamingos are what Samuel had in mind when he said to 'find some influential animals.' Besides, they're from Miami," Frieda replied. "And what's wrong with our local flamingos or a nice roseate spoonbill leading the walk? Not to mention that the *Miami* flamingos are asking for a *dressing room* and they absolutely refuse to start before ten a.m. They said it's in their contract." The big bird finished with a huff and flew off.

Bu Zard opened his red backpack with his beak and rummaged through papers, looking for the flamingos' contract.

"Bu Zard, I—." Elda, the mother bear was still trying to speak to Bu Zard. She moved around the vulture, attempting to get his attention. But the vulture kept turning away from her. The pair had soon made a circle. Bu Zard was so intent on avoiding the bear, he didn't notice that some of his papers fell to the ground.

"I'm sorry, Elda. There's something I must take care of," he said. Then, without giving the mother bear a chance to say another word, he flew away.

Elda watched the disappearing bird for a moment. Then she motioned to her cubs and took off running in the same direction.

The opossum shows his claws

Desta arrived before sunrise with her aunt and twenty-two turtle cousins. They were immediately led to the back of the line by a cackling wood stork who called herself Betty.

"Turtles will be lining up here. Ahumm." The wood stork stared at the long list she had in her hand. She pulled it up close to her eyes. "Oh, yes. You are with the alligators and crocodiles. I can't read Frieda's writing, mainly because she has scratched through the snakes over and over. Obviously, she couldn't decide where to put them."

Desta followed the wood stork as she had been told. "Guess I won't be near the deer," the turtle said, thinking out loud about her friends Sophie and Tony.

"Oh, no, most definitely not," said Betty. "This will be an orderly march! When the time comes to start, we will all line up with our species and proceed accordingly. The deer are near the front of the line, and you are with the reptiles at the back of the line. Well, almost. The snakes are at the very back.

"Don't forget, we will be conducting a safety meeting in thirty minutes. And we will give out your alligator assignment. All of you smaller turtles will be riding on the backs of the largest alligators," Betty said before hurrying away.

This was good news for Desta, who was glad she would *not* have to march the entire way to Tallahassee, thereby saving her feet, which were more like small swim fins.

So far, everything had been a new experience for the soft-shell turtle on this first trip out of the Everglades. This wasn't surprising since she was not that old for a turtle. In people years, she was twelve.

Desta showed up right on time for the safety meeting, and a bright orange spot was painted in the middle of her shell. This stirred up a few protests about the color from Desta's aunt and cousins.

"Safety, safety," Betty, the wood stork, told them. "The color identifies you as a participant in the march."

After the safety meeting, Desta found her alligator assignment and spent the rest of the morning watching all the activity around her. Sometimes, she watched from deep inside her shell, and sometimes the excitement of the adventure took over and she stuck her head way out, twisting every which way to see what was going on around her. It was while she had her head out, looking around, that she spotted the opossum.

He stood very still in the middle of a group of frogs and lizards lined up ahead of the turtles and alligators. Desta knew he wasn't supposed to be there. He was a mammal and the group he had joined was made up of amphibians. The more she watched him, the more suspicious she became. Desta could not take her eyes off of him. The opossum stood like a statue, his eyes glued to the side of the road. The turtle was too short to see what the opossum was watching, so she began making her way through the crowd, getting closer and closer to the disagreeable animal, the whole time wondering what he was up to. She was so busy watching the opossum, she almost missed the reason he was standing there. But as she moved toward him, the arrival of a blue heron caught Desta's eye.

Bu Zard! And his friends! Desta realized they were in the opossum's direct line of sight. She crawled closer to watch the vulture who was talking to a large black bear. The blue heron stood behind Bu Zard, waved her wings around, and then flew away.

Bu Zard spun in circles, pulling papers from his red backpack that looked like Desta's school book bag. The bear was trying to get in front of him, but no matter which way she went, Bu Zard turned the other. He was so busy moving away from the mother bear that he didn't notice the papers sliding from his bag onto the ground.

But Desta noticed. And she knew the opossum had noticed too. As soon as Bu Zard and the bear left, the opossum ran straight to the place Bu Zard had stood, scooped up the vulture's papers, and ran to the pine forest beside the road.

Desta followed carefully behind the animal, ready to pull her head into her shell if the opossum looked around.

The turtle arrived at the edge of the trees in time to watch the opossum studying Bu Zard's lost papers. He glanced around nervously. When he thought the coast was clear and he was not being watched, the opossum made smudge marks all over the stolen pages. Then he dipped his claw in mud and re-drew the lines he had just smudged. He did this to each of the sheets he had retrieved from the pack. Then he quickly folded them back together and ran in the same direction the vulture had flown moments before.

Desta looked around for a turtle she might tell. She spotted her aunt and her twenty-two cousins lining up on the backs of alligators that were waiting for instructions.

"Hey," she called to them. "Wait for me."

Wide-eyed and breathing hard, the little turtle crawled over to the group. "We have to do something," she said. "The opossum has taken Bu Zard's papers. He's up to something. He has to be stopped!"

"Desta, you get up here right now!" Desta's aunt snapped at her. "Your mother told you to stay with your species. What were you doing with that nasty opossum? How many times have you been told to mind your own business and keep your head in your shell? Huh, how many?" her aunt asked impatiently.

But Desta was not listening to her aunt. She had to tell Bu Zard. Ignoring her aunt, she turned and headed in the same direction as the blue heron, the turkey vulture, the black bear, and the opossum.

Chapter 9

Friends Reunited

"Desta, wait up!"

The turtle turned to see who had called her name, then watched as Tony jumped over a family of armadillos digging for bugs among the palmettos along the side of the road.

"Wait, where are you going in such a hurry?" he asked Desta.

Sophie came right behind Tony. She jumped over the armadillos and narrowly missed running into the back of her brother when he stopped suddenly.

Desta turned her attention back to crawling as quickly as her short legs and webbed feet could take her. She weaved among the animals, moving farther and farther away from her family, focusing on her mission to tell Bu Zard about his dropped papers.

"Tony, you are so in trouble. We're supposed to be following Mom and Dad, not turtles," said Sophie. Then, turning to Desta, the deer asked, "Where *are* you going? I thought you wanted to stay with your family."

Desta kept crawling while she answered Sophie's question. "I'm going to find Bu Zard. I have important information I have to tell him."

"You're in luck," said Tony. "We're going to find him ourselves. Well, really Dad is. We're just following along. So, do you want to go with us?"

"What information?" asked Sophie, cutting off her brother before he could say anything else. "Why is it important? Can you tell us?"

"I just watched that opossum take Bu Zard's papers, papers that fell out of that red backpack he carries."

"So what?" said Tony. "He's probably taking the papers back to Bu Zard."

"Maybe," said Desta. "But he made some changes to them first."

Tony looked at his sister. A silent message passed between the siblings, and Sophie shook her head back and forth.

"*Toneeeeee*," Sophie said through clenched teeth. "Mom will kill you if you get involved."

"We're just helping out a friend, Soph," he said. "We're still following Mom and Dad. You lead the way, and Desta and I will follow."

Desta was not paying attention to the deer. She was going to find Bu Zard whether they went or not. She shook her turtle head and tried to concentrate on crawling around all the animals lined up along the road. This wasn't easy. The animals were waving signs and practicing chants. She looked back at her new friends. Maybe she could use their help getting through.

The Croc Brothers, who had dressed in identical orange vests and baseball caps, led the animals in cheers by yelling through a large megaphone while standing on one side of the road.

On the other side of the road, an enthusiastic group of mammals jumped up and down, waving their signs and shouting, "USA, USA! We are the *United Species of Animals*!"

"Give me a G!" yelled Larry, the oldest Croc Brother.

"G," shouted the animals led by the two younger brothers.

"Give me an O," the crocodile shouted and then continued. "Give me a G-R-E-E-N. What does that spell? *GOOOOO Green*. Say it again. *Go Green*!"

"Save our planet! Save our 'Glades! *Save our water!*" screamed a group of animals trying to outdo the Croc Brothers.

Desta and Tony were blocked by the chanting animals and their signs. No matter which way the two tried to move, the cheering animals moved in front of them, in some cases almost trampling Desta. When the two friends finally got through the chanting crowd and looked around, Sophie had disappeared from sight.

Tony jumped up and down a few times trying to locate his sister. If she found their mom and dad without him, he'd probably get in trouble. After a moment of looking, he lowered his head to the turtle. "This way, Desta. I'll get us to Bu Zard."

Chapter 10

The Problems Start with Pink

Bu Zard stood with the flamingos who were still dressing for the occasion. The pink birds powdered their beaks while adjusting their boas and tiaras as Frieda fumed nearby.

"I just don't understand what the problem is," said the tallest flamingo who introduced herself as Kandee. "Spelled with a K! We're very famous birds. Why, we've been on TV and in several well-known movies. Our mothers were even on a TV series called *Miami Vice*. I'm sure you've heard of that. Raquel, Rome, Lola, and I feel like you should be grateful to have us as your celebrity guests of honor."

"Yes," said Raquel. "And there are statues of us in thousands of yards all over Florida. We're famous. Very."

"Yes, very," repeated Rome, as she threw her boa over her shoulder and held her head high.

Frieda almost choked. Bu Zard held his wing in front of her to keep her reaction from the four divas.

"Girls," he said. "How can we help? What can we do to make this trip as easy as possible? Of course, we want you to be comfortable. Right, Frieda? Frieda?"

“And there are statues of us in thousands of yards all over Florida. We’re famous.”

Bu Zard turned to where his assistant had been standing, but she was stomping away in Samuel's direction, no doubt to complain about the flamingos.

Bu Zard turned back to the pink birds. "Take your time, girls. Do what you need to do to prepare for our trip. We still have a few glitches to iron out before we get going. You all look marvelous, just simply gorgeous," he told the preening birds from over his shoulder as he hurried after Frieda.

Frieda had gone straight to Samuel and was, in true blue heron fashion, giving him an earful when Bu Zard arrived.

"I will not wait on a bunch of over-feathered, long-necked, skinny, pink birds. They have no business leading our march!" Frieda screeched at Samuel. "They don't even know *why* there *is* a march. All they care about are TV cameras and parades. I am furious with Bu Zard."

Bu Zard hurried to Frieda. In her anger, she seemed to have forgotten her fear of the alligator and was leaning closer and closer to the large snout and the mouth lined with teeth.

"Frieda!" shouted Bu Zard. "Frieda, we need to get our walk moving. We have to be in Immokalee before two o'clock. We have our lunch wagons and a TV crew from Channel 7 News meeting us there. Snap, snap, let's go."

Frieda and Samuel both turned to glare at Bu Zard and were ready to give him an earful. But they never got the chance.

At that very moment, two handsome, adult deer jumped over a group of mammals waiting close to Bu Zard and Samuel. The deer slowed and walked gracefully to the three leaders of the march.

The larger deer, a buck with a full rack of antlers, stopped and lowered his head in a slight nod. "We've come to help, however you can use us," he said.

"Victor, Wanda, glad you could make it," Bu Zard turned slightly toward Samuel and nodded his head toward the two deer. "Here they are, two more of our influential recruits," the vulture said, hoping to turn Samuel and Frieda's attention away from the flamingos.

Before Samuel could say a word, Elda, the mother bear, came pushing through the same animals that Victor and Wanda had just jumped over.

"Whoa, whoa, whoa," said a young bobcat that had been lying lazily in the sun. "First, I've got deer flying over me. Next, a crazed bear is running across the top of me. This is no way to treat a cat."

Elda mumbled back, "Sorry," then lumbered to a stop in front of Bu Zard.

The bobcat followed Elda to the circle of animals around Bu Zard that was growing larger by the moment.

"Elda, no, we can't do it," the vulture said, without giving her a chance to ask.

"What's going on now?" asked Samuel, while looking from Bu Zard to the mother bear and back to Frieda. "What's she talking about?"

"It's my son, Jason. He's in danger. He's in the city, turning over trashcans, crashing through backyards. He was even in someone's kitchen. If he's caught, he will be put to death. He has two strikes already. If we take him to Tallahassee with us, we can ask the Governor to pardon him."

Samuel listened to the mother bear tell her story. Then he asked, "What can we do Elda? We can't take all these animals through the city on a search. We'll lose half of them. We'll also draw attention to him. If we find Jason, so will everyone else. Do you want to risk that?"

"We have to do something," said Elda, clasping her paws together and pleading with the group. "I can't go alone with my cubs. The wildlife control officers will take me. I need help."

"*Tch, tch, tch*, the one thing we definitely do not need," said Frieda, "is an out of control bear getting bad publicity. How are we going to be taken seriously if lone animals are out there making public spectacles of themselves?"

"Now just a minute," said Elda, stepping forward to defend her son. "He was doing fine till you two got him mixed up in all the protest stuff. Bu Zard, you told him to take a stand."

Samuel's eyes grew round and his tail made a swish across the ground.

"Wait, wait! I didn't mean for him to go out and break into houses. But let's all calm down and just think for a minute here. I'm sure if we put our heads together, we can think of something," said Bu Zard. He was feeling a little guilty after listening to the mother bear's pleas for help. "The timing on this is very bad. We need to get control of the bear. But what do we do?"

"I'll go," interrupted Victor.

Wanda looked startled. "Victor?"

"It's all right, Wanda. I'm fast. I can get in, get him, and get him out," Victor said. "I'll take him out the back way. We'll go through the Hammock and up the Gulf coast. We can avoid people and meet all of you in Tallahassee."

Elda heaved a sigh of relief. "I won't forget this, Victor," she told the big buck.

Bu Zard felt a small weight lift off his shoulders. Thank goodness they'd found half a solution. Finding the bear would be easy. Getting him to leave town to meet the Animal March in Tallahassee would not be that easy. Jason was one stubborn bear who had left the Everglades very angry after his home was destroyed by the heavy machines. The news media was sure to play up the bear once the animals were on the road. They could even point him out as a troublemaker and make a comparison to the Animal March. It would not help their cause if Jason was causing problems and giving humans a bad impression of animals.

"Do what you can to get him out of there," said Bu Zard.

"I'm in too," said the bobcat who, until this moment had been standing quietly beside Bu Zard. Then, while stretching out his paw in front of his face and showing each of his five claws, he continued, "I'm definitely in. This marching thing is not my bag. But sneaking around the city, doing some undercover secret stuff, has me written all over it."

"I don't need any help, but thank you," said Victor. "I don't need to be slowed down or responsible for *two* animals."

The bobcat snickered. "I guess your plan is to trot your big deer self, antlers and all, right down Main Street," the cat purred. Then he stretched again and walked into the middle of the group. "Look," he said. "I've got experience sneaking around. It's what I do. To show you what a cool cat I am, I'll go with you. My name's Maurice, and you need me."

Before Victor could say no, Wanda accepted the offer for him. "Yes, of course, Maurice. Victor would love to have your help," she said to the cat, and then she turned to Victor. "If you're going to do this dangerous mission, at least take an animal that is offering to help you and knows the area."

Victor looked from the cat to Wanda and back to the cat again. "All right," said Victor, choosing not to argue with Wanda. "We need to move fast. We won't have the protection of the group. We stay off the roads and in the woods as much as possible."

"That's settled then." Bu Zard threw up his wings to end the conversation and get back to a bigger problem for him at the moment: the march. How was he going to get the animals started?

Bu Zard turned back to Frieda. "Okay, we've got that problem under control. Now let's get this show on the road. I've got our maps right here."

Bu Zard shuffled through his pouch, searching for the trip maps he had put together with the help of Benson, the bald eagle and Frieda. They had spent the last two weeks flying the routes, looking for the safest roads to take the animals through the state and to Tallahassee.

"Frieda, do you have the maps?" he asked as he looked though his pack.

Frieda squawked. "You said you'd handle the maps. Remember, Bu Zard? You wanted to lead the march, you and those flea-bitten pink fluffs," she mumbled as she turned on her heel and flew away.

Bu Zard pulled papers frantically from his bag, throwing them onto the ground, followed by pencils and snacks, until finally, he threw the empty backpack into the air.

The vulture spun in circles looking at his mess, not noticing the opossum that watched him from behind a flock of white ibis.

Frieda will most certainly not let me forget this. She has a tendency to remember my mess-ups. And Samuel . . . Bu Zard shuttered at the thought. He kicked at the empty backpack.

"Mr. Buzzard! Oh, Mr. Turkey Buzzard. There you are. I've been searching all over for you. Thank goodness I found you."

Bu Zard glanced around for the animal calling him. Seeing the annoying opossum, he turned to pick up his empty backpack.

T.J. approached Bu Zard, pushing the altered maps toward him. "Mr. Buzzard?"

"*Bu Zard* or Mr. Vulture, if you don't mind," Bu Zard said.

"You dropped these papers. I've been looking for you," the opossum replied, a coy look on his face.

Bu Zard glanced at the papers and realized what the opossum was offering him. He grabbed the maps from the outstretched claws, barely containing his relief as he waved them in the air.

"Thank you, thank you!" he said, as he danced in circles. Then, realizing the opossum was still watching him, he stopped and repeated, "Thank you. I am glad you found them. These are our maps to Tallahassee, and without the maps, we might wander off course or miss our food stops."

T.J. smiled and shrugged his shoulders as if his actions were nothing important. "Just wanted to help with the march and make my contribution. If you need anything—anything at all—you just yell for me. Call me T.J., short for Terrence Jr. Family name, you know," he said, as he backed away from the vulture.

Bu Zard watched the opossum hurry away, his bald tail in the air, twitching back and forth as he disappeared into the midst of the animals. Then the much-relieved vulture began repacking his backpack.

Chapter 11
The Meeting in the Woods

It took much longer than Desta had planned to find Bu Zard. Tony was not much help and easily distracted. First, they'd been stopped by a large bear named Fidel, who insisted on spraying Tony with orange safety paint, something Desta had made sure she had gotten done for herself upon arrival that morning. Next, Betty, the wood stork, draped a rope over Tony's back that held a sign with the letters USA on each side. Then she lectured them both about the dead zone she had heard was creeping across the Gulf of Mexico.

"I'm telling you," she said, while pointing the tip of her wing at them. "Things aren't like the old days. It's a scary world we live in. Bacteria are floating across the Gulf, killing all the fish. Giant snakes everywhere. People in every corner of the 'Glades staring at me through those binocular things hanging around their necks. I'm afraid to take a bath. I don't know if I'm going to be eaten by a giant snake or spied on by a peeping person hiding in the bushes."

The wood stork was still talking as Desta and Tony walked away.

Desta finally reached the limit of her patience when Tony shook off his signs and stopped to take part in a chant and dance that was being arranged by the rodent crew.

Mice, rats, chipmunks, and squirrels all danced and spun in circles. Behind the dancers, rows of beavers and otters kept beat with wooden sticks. They were all hoping to get on TV. "We've practiced for weeks," they told Desta.

Desta sighed and was about to continue alone to find Bu Zard, when Tony spun in the opposite direction of the other dancers and almost crushed a flying squirrel. The rodent crew was not amused and shooed the deer away.

"*Now* can you focus on getting us through the animals?" Desta asked.

Tony did not respond and Desta stomped her small turtle foot in frustration.

Tony dropped his head down beside Desta's. "Look over there," he whispered. "What do you see?"

Desta could not see around the animals, and she was too short to see over them. "Nothing," she said with a hiss.

Tony waded through a family of raccoons, opening up a passage for the turtle to see through.

T.J. stood at the edge of the woods. He looked first to his right and then to his left, as if to make sure he wasn't being followed. Then he slipped into the pine forest that lined the road out of the Everglades.

Desta and Tony strained to see if the opossum was still in possession of the papers Bu Zard had dropped. But T.J. disappeared into the woods.

"What do you want to do?" asked Tony.

Desta was already on the move. “Come on! Let’s follow him.”

They walked cautiously to the spot they had last seen the thief. Very slowly, and as discreetly as possible, they followed the opossum into the woods.

The wooded area they entered was an upland slash pine forest. The sandy floor of the forest was covered in palmetto plants and small cabbage palms, all of which helped to block the path the opossum had taken.

Desta and Tony moved cautiously into the forest, not knowing what they would find. They placed one foot in front of the other, moving quietly until they heard voices. The first voice they heard was the opossum. The other voice was faint and harder to hear, so the two small animals moved closer in order to hear their conversation.

“I’m telling you, they are not going to make it to Tallahassee,” the opossum said. “They’ll be so mad at that turkey buzzard within two days—three days, tops—that they’ll be ready to rip him apart. If my first plan doesn’t work, you can hit them from the air. Bring everything you’ve got. I’m sure we can convince them there are better things to do than to continue following the buzzard’s half-baked plan.”

Desta moved close enough to see that the other voice belonged to a human.

The stranger responded to T.J.’s reassurances, “Yeah, but so far, this half-baked plan has brought together a very large group of animals. They’ve also managed to arouse the curiosity of the media. If they get this crazy show on the road, there’ll be others sympathetic to their cause. You better do something or else! My bosses cannot afford this!"

"We can always go to the relocation plan," said the opossum.

"TONY! Where are you?" Sophie yelled, sounding as if she were right behind them.

Desta squeaked and looked around quickly. Tony started backing out of the woods toward his sister's voice. When the turtle looked back, the opossum was gone and the man was looking right at her. His hat was pulled low over his eyes, and a blue tie with yellow half-moons on it lay flat against his shirt. He pointed at her. Then he turned and fled into the woods. The last thing she saw of the man was his tie flapping back over his shoulder.

"Tony, you are so in trouble," Sophie was telling her brother when Desta emerged from the woods. "We've been looking for you. The little flying squirrel over there, who is now being carried by the fox squirrel, said you stepped on him then ran into these woods."

"Sophie! Sophie, you've got to listen."

"Mom said she's going to put you on a short rope and tie you to her if you don't stop running off. Desta, how did you let him talk you into following him?" Sophie continued with her scolding.

"But, Sophie, we've got to talk to the turkey vulture," said Tony, "The opossum—"

"The opossum? You've got to be kidding me! I don't want to hear any more about the opossum. You and that turtle need to get off the opossum thing. Mom! Tony was chasing the opossum!" Sophie yelled to her mother.

"But the papers," said Desta. "We have to tell Bu Zard the opossum has his papers."

"No, the opossum gave Bu Zard his stuff," said Sophie. "And now Bu Zard is at the front of the line, getting ready to start the walk. We have to find our species. It's in the rules."

Tony gave Desta an apologetic look and shook his head. "Sorry, Desta. I've got to go with my mom." Tony followed his sister for a few steps then whispered over his shoulder, "Find me later. We need to talk."

Desta watched as Tony followed his sister and mother to find a place to stand at the front of the line after being given a thorough reprimand. Then she turned to start the long walk to join her cousins on the backs of alligators. She was probably going to be in trouble with her aunt, but she had no doubt that something bad was going on with that opossum.

Let the march begin

"Attention, attention, everyone. We're ready to start our march. *Are you ready?*" Bu Zard yelled to the gathered animals.

"*Yes!*" responded the crowd of animals waving their signs and jumping up and down.

"I said, *are you ready*?!" Bu Zard yelled again. His voice boomed through the crowd and the animals responded with enthusiasm and gusto.

"*Yes, we are!*" screamed the animals.

Bu Zard looked out into the middle of the crowd. The animals started a cheer that was repeated throughout the group.

"USA, USA! Save our water! Save our animals! Save our Everglades!"

The Croc Brothers were leading a conga line through the crowd. The group dancing with them grew larger as more marchers joined in.

The scene was impressive. Hundreds of animals had gathered for this march. The enthusiasm was contagious. The crowd began to move forward, led by four strutting pink flamingos and the turkey vulture.

Bu Zard thrust his chest out and waved his wings up and down. He'd done it. He'd actually done it. The Animal March had begun.

Two days to turn them around

Two figures stood in the cover of the forest. The man took picture after picture of the large group of animals as they walked by. The front of the line was mixed with mammals and birds followed by amphibians and reptiles. The snakes were at the end of the line and the last group to pass by.

"This march is big," said the man. "Much bigger than what we thought it would be. This will definitely make an impression on the Governor and his legislature, if they get very far."

"Don't worry," said T.J.

"Two days I'll give you to get them turned around. If your plan doesn't work, I'll handle them. I won't hesitate to start relocation plans."

Chapter 12
Wrong Way

Bu Zard scratched his featherless head with the end of his wing and looked around. By one o'clock, the Animal March, which had gotten off to a great start, already had difficulties. The lunch wagons were nowhere in sight and the animals were complaining. He scanned the sky looking for Benson and Della who were in charge of the food.

The temperatures along the road were more than eighty-five degrees. The animals were tired and ready for a break in their march. The roads they had traveled along so far were long and straight with little traffic. Every once in a while, a pickup truck loaded with vegetables or a tractor with its plow in the raised position came along. Then the animals all moved to the side of the road, waved their signs at the passing vehicles, and chanted "USA, USA! Save the 'Glades and save our water."

Bu Zard could not help but overhear the deer family complaining as they walked behind him.

"Mom, I'm hungry," said Sophie. It was the third time in thirty minutes she'd made the statement.

"Sophie, honey, please, this is only the first day and the first four hours. You're going to have to be a little more patient," Wanda said to her daughter.

"Gee, Mom, are we there yet?" Tony giggled, teasing his mother.

"Seriously, Mom," said Sophie. "When are we stopping? I feel like I've been walking for days," she added dramatically.

Frieda flew down and landed beside Bu Zard; her long neck moved back and forth as they walked. But before she could open her beak to talk, one of the pink flamingos started to complain.

"Bu Zard," said Kandee whose tiara had slid to the side of her head, and her boa dragged on the ground. "Where are the TV cameras and news reporters? We thought they'd be here by now. Did you tell them *we* are leading the walk?"

"Soon, ladies, soon," he said reassuringly. "We have a long way to go and there'll be plenty of time for your interviews with the news media."

"Bu Zard, I thought we were stopping at noon to have lunch and rest," Frieda said to him, dismissing the flamingos and their complaints. "The animals are asking for a lunch break."

"We can't. We're not there yet," he stated simply. Then, looking annoyed, he checked his maps for the umpteenth time. Something wasn't right. They should've been at the lunch stop already. Bu Zard didn't want Frieda to know he was worried, but they must have made a wrong turn.

Frieda wasn't going to be put off. She walked in front of the vulture, forcing him to stop and listen. "Bu Zard, we have to break. The animals are hungry and it's lunchtime. They'll eat each other!"

"Everything's fine, Frieda. Just keep saying that and they'll believe you," said Bu Zard.

"That's your plan? Oh, good grief! Where's Samuel?" Frieda hurried away just as Benson and Della flew in and landed.

"Bu Zard, why are you going this way? It's not one of the routes we discussed," Benson told him. "We'll never make the afternoon press conference."

"My maps are correct," answered Bu Zard. "I drew the maps as we flew the routes. I just think walking it is a lot different than flying. We'll be at our lunch stop soon." Then he added a quick, "I hope," under his breath.

"Only if you're planning on lunching in Fort Lauderdale," said Della. "We've been heading east all morning."

"I'm telling you, it's not like flying. You can't just walk through trees. You have to go around them and follow the road," Bu Zard said with a touch of irritation in his voice.

"Well, we've got to get some food in here," said Benson. "Come on, Della, we need some help."

As soon as the eagles left, Bu Zard took off and flew above the road to see for himself where they were. As soon as he got above the treetops, he knew they were off course. Gazing down over the ground below, he could pick out familiar landmarks recognizable once he was in the air. From the road, everything ran together, the slash pine forests, one after another, followed by acres of palm nurseries, and fields of tomatoes and sugar cane. They had passed miles of farmland where signs for HM Consolidated Enterprises had been placed every five hundred feet. It was all part of the South Florida landscape lining every road that led out of the Everglades.

Once he returned to the ground, he pulled the maps from his red backpack to review once again. Mumbling to himself, he turned the map around and around to figure out where he had gone wrong. How could this happen?

"Bu Zard?" Samuel crawled up behind the distracted vulture. "Is there anything wrong? I'm hearing a lot of grumbling around me."

"Oh, no, everything's great. We're just waiting on Benson to get the food trucks here," Bu Zard tried to reassure the alligator. And himself.

Samuel would definitely not be happy if he knew the truth. Bu Zard now depended on Benson to get the food to them, and he hoped it would be quick. He couldn't let the animals know they were heading in the wrong direction. And above all else, he had to act like he knew what he was doing. No sense admitting that they'd already made a wrong turn. He could not lose their confidence in the first four hours of the march.

Opossum playing 'possum

The afternoon moved slowly and, by two o'clock, it was evident that the animals wouldn't make the parade or the lunch wagon waiting for them in the town of Immokalee. There was obvious confusion within the leadership. Bu Zard had flown off several times and then returned to the front of the march to argue with Frieda.

Tony nudged his sister. "Sophie, let's get closer to Bu Zard and see what's going on," he whispered. "There's something happening and I want to see what it is."

"Are you nuts, Tony? Mom will have your deer hide if you disappear again."

The siblings were too busy arguing to notice the dead opossum on the side of the road. They passed within feet of the creature lying still in a clump of wildflowers.

The other animals following the deer did notice, so they walked on the road to avoid the poor animal that hadn't made the crossing safely. A group of black vultures, however, made a point of walking close.

"We don't want to look like a bunch of heartless vultures, now, do we?" asked Johnson, the leader. "None of the other animals have had lunch. Let's circle around and wait till they've all passed. This is fresh meat. Stay close, boys. I think *our* lunch wagon has arrived."

T.J. shifted a tiny bit in the clump of flowers where he was lying. "Hey! I'm taking a nap," he snapped at the big black birds, startling the group.

T.J. had strategically placed himself along the side of the road. *Playing 'possum*—which meant he was playing dead—was his favorite game. Playing it now, he could listen to the animals that passed close by. Everything he overheard he would report back to his employers. Things were definitely going his way. He could report how quickly the animals had started complaining about the vulture's leadership.

This could be over in a day if he played his cards right.

Two major hurdles

Miles to the north of the marching animals, Victor and Maurice were making better progress on their mission to rescue Jason, who was in trouble and a potential problem for the Animal March. Since they didn't have to follow roads and they could avoid the cities, their trip north could be much faster than the other animals.

The two stopped to rest beside one of the hundreds of fruit trees planted in neat rows in an orange grove. "Woo wee," Maurice purred. "Now that was a run. We're above Lake Okeechobee by now."

The big buck ignored Maurice, choosing instead to look around their resting place and to sniff the air, gauging for himself where they were.

Maurice smiled and continued to talk. "Of course, this *is* the easiest part of the trip. The toughest part is yet to come. Finding the bear is only a fraction of our problems." Maurice looked over at Victor as he finished his sentence to see if the big buck was listening.

Victor spoke for the first time since leaving the other animals. "Look, Maurice. That is your name, right? You *are* fast and you've been able to keep up so far. I don't really have much time for small talk, so if you have something to say, say it. Otherwise, we'll rest for a moment then get going again."

Maurice laughed. "Yeah, I noticed you tried to lose me in a couple of spots. But you might want to keep me around. We've got two big hurdles before we get to Ocala. I'm your best chance for getting around both of them."

"I'm listening," said Victor.

"The first problem is I-4. It's a large, heavily traveled interstate, day and night. It cuts across the state between Orlando and Tampa. I know a few underpasses we can use to get to the other side."

"Okay, not too big a deal. What else?" Victor asked.

"There's a gang, a very large gang, of coyotes that control all of the area north of Orlando and south of Ocala. They have splinter groups, and they are a mean, angry pack of animals."

Victor nodded, thought about it for a moment, and then spoke. "We go through at night and just keep our eyes open. We should be able to avoid them if we don't make a lot of noise while passing through."

"You don't understand," said Maurice. "They already know we're coming."

Chapter 13
More Than One Problem

Desta knew that they had serious problems within the Animal March. She had tried to tell several of her family members about the man in the woods, but not one turtle would listen to her. After being told to shush several times, she gave up and decided to find Tony. Maybe the two of them could talk to an adult. By the time she reached her friends, it was obvious there were a lot of problems, food being the main one. Food was always an issue for the animals.

Tony and Sophie seemed glad to see Desta and began telling her about their morning as soon as the turtle had made her way to them.

"What's happening?" Desta asked. "What happened to 'save the 'Glades' and 'go green'? Every animal I passed was arguing or angry."

"We're lost," Sophie said very matter of fact.

"We're not lost, Sophie," Tony told his sister. "We know exactly where we are. I heard the bald eagles tell Bu Zard that we're on our way to Fort Lauderdale."

"*If* we were headed to the beach, that would be good, but since we're supposed to be headed north, . . . ummm, not so good," said Desta, confirming Sophie's feeling about the situation. "I know the opossum had something to do with this. We've got to tell someone what we heard this morning, Tony."

"What did you hear this morning?" asked Sophie.

"*Uhhh*, that's what I tried to tell you," said Tony, "before you told Mom on me. Desta and I followed the opossum into the woods."

"I don't want to hear this if it's about the opossum. You two are going to get in trouble."

"No, listen, Sophie," Tony said.

"La, la, la, la."

Desta put her small foot against Sophie's leg to get the deer's attention.

Sophie stopped singing and looked down at the turtle.

"We saw the opossum with a man," said Desta.

"*A what?!*" screamed Sophie. "You better not tell Mom, she'll be really mad that you were in the woods with a human."

"Oh yeah, well, that's not all," said Tony. "They were planning an attack."

Hit them from the air

Nearby, Samuel could hear everything that Tony and Desta were telling Sophie. His huge tail moved back and forth in agitation as their story unfolded. The more the younger animals said, the faster his tail moved, sending sand and dust into the air.

Bu Zard spotted the dust bowl, which was turning into a small cyclone, and knew it meant trouble. "Girls, keep the walk going. There's something I need to check on," he told the diva flamingos as he high-tailed it over to the big alligator.

"What's wrong, Samuel?" Bu Zard asked, and then because he was nervous, he began talking very fast. "I know we got off to a slow start, but we've corrected the problem, and I know, any minute now, we should have some information from Benson and Della and we—"

"Bu Zard, we have a much bigger problem than heading in the wrong direction!" Samuel roared. "I didn't hear everything, but according to those children we may be attacked!"

Samuel quickly told Bu Zard the things he had overheard.

Wanda, the mother deer, had noticed the irate alligator and was in the process of moving her children and Desta away from him as quickly as possible when Bu Zard landed beside them.

"Kids, kids, wait a minute. Samuel wants to talk to you."

Wanda stared at Bu Zard with a horrified expression. "I'm sure he's not talking about these children, Bu Zard. They've been right beside me this entire time and I know they have *not* . . . " She trailed off in her response, probably because she wasn't sure of *what* the kids had not done.

"It's all right, Wanda," Bu Zard said reassuringly. "Your children might have information that is important to the group. Samuel only wants to speak to them."

The small group stepped off to the side, allowing the other animals to pass them in the march.

Wanda cocked her head to one side, frowned, and then positioned herself between Samuel and the children.

"We have a much bigger problem."

Bu Zard began questioning the young animals. "What's this story about a man in the woods this morning? And who's planning an attack? What exactly did you see and hear?"

The children began talking all at once.

Bu Zard blew his whistle. "All right!" he shouted. "One-at-a-time. Turtle girl, you start."

"I'm, I'm, uh, Desta, sir," she stammered, and then began telling the vulture and the alligator about the opossum she had first met in the gumbo-limbo tree.

Tony finished telling the story and when he got to the part where the man in the blue tie with yellow half-moons told the opossum to take care of the problem or else, Samuel and Bu Zard both took a step closer to hear the deer speak.

"Or else what?" the two asked together.

"Or else he would take care of the problem," said Tony. "The man in the tie said he would hit us from the air."

Desta spoke, her tiny turtle voice barely audible over the loud voices of the adults. "I saw him change your maps, Mr. Vulture."

"He *what*?"

Desta repeated her sentence and added, "They said they have a relocation plan."

"What does that mean?" asked Bu Zard. Then he repeated in disbelief, "What does relocation plan mean?"

He looked at the mother deer whose mouth was hanging open.

Finally, she managed to get the words out. "It means that I'm taking my children and going home," she said with a determined look in her eye. "You too, Desta. I'm sure your mother would want you out of danger."

"Mo-om," Tony whined. "What happened to saving our water? What happened to meeting Dad? He'll be all alone in Tallahassee."

Bu Zard's shoulders dropped, his wings dipping to the ground, his mind racing to think of a way to stop this news from spreading among the animals.

Before the vulture could present his argument, a startling, loud noise came from the distance. The birds nearby rose in large flocks and flew into the sky, circling the marching animals, then returned to the ground and their places.

A small speck of red appeared on the straight, flat road in the distance. Beyond the speck, flying low in the sky, were two more specks even tinier than the one on the road.

Bu Zard thought of the story he had just heard from the deer and turtle. *An attack from the air! Could this be happening? And what on earth are those specks in the sky? Small missiles?*

Bu Zard panicked. "This is it!" he shouted to the animals around him. "We're under attack! Listen to the noise. We have to tell everyone to hide!" The turkey vulture ran toward the front of the line, yelling at every animal he passed to take cover and hide.

Frieda and the divas were leading the group. The blue heron was walking on one side of the road and the pink flamingos were on the other. Their dislike for each other was growing by the moment. The stalemate of not talking was broken, however, when Bu Zard passed them all.

"Hide!" Bu Zard yelled while running past the birds. "Hide! We're under attack!" Then he dove, head first, into a clump of palmettos on the side of the road, ignoring the sharp blades of the plant.

"What is *his* problem?" asked Kandee.

This question was directed to Frieda who now stood beside the palmetto bush, staring down at Bu Zard's feet sticking out between the blades.

"It must be the heat and lack of food," said Rome, making her own observation with a touch of sarcasm in her voice. "And what is that racket up ahead? It's coming right for us."

The specks of red were much closer by this time and the noise grew louder. Horns were honking and bells were ringing.

"Bu Zard," Frieda said. "Bu Zard, have you had a heat stroke? What are you doing?"

"What does it look like I'm doing? You need to hide too, Frieda. Tell the flamingos to head for Miami. We're in danger."

"Gladly," said Frieda. "But first tell me why we're in danger?" Frieda grabbed Bu Zard's foot with her beak and tried to pull him from the bush he was holding on to.

"The opossum and a man in a tie are attacking us from the air. They want to stop the march. They are coming *now*!"

Lola and Kandee were now standing beside Frieda. They gave each other a look and shook their heads in bewilderment. They bent down and gabbed Bu Zard's other foot with their beaks and pulled, along with Frieda.

The birds could hear Bu Zard's breathing. He was sucking air so fast he would probably hyperventilate if he didn't stop. The three pulled harder.

Bu Zard could not hold on to the bush any longer. He let go, causing the three birds pulling his feet to fall backward. In the tumble, the flamingos lost their tiaras and most of their dignity.

"Bu Zard, those are our food wagons," Frieda said impatiently as she struggled to get back to her feet. "Della and Benson went to find food. Remember? Get your head out from under your wing and look."

Bu Zard looked in the direction of Frieda's outstretched wing and realized she was right. Benson and Della were leading the small caravan of red wagons into a newly plowed field to the left of the marching animals. They turned beside a large sign that read HM CONSOLIDATED FARMS and then came to a stop in the middle of the field. The sign they passed was the size of a billboard with a site plan of a future development in the bottom right corner. A picture of a bright yellow half-moon was in the top left corner of the sign. On the far side of the field, a canal—a long, skinny, man-made canal—stretched as far as the vulture could see.

Bu Zard felt silly and jumped up from the ground, brushing the dirt off of himself with his wings.

"Of course, of course," said the turkey vulture. "I'm aware of what we're doing. I am the leader, remember."

"*You're* the one who needs to remember," said Frieda. "So far, your leadership has been erratic and . . . and . . . " She turned to look in the direction Bu Zard was looking.

A Croc Brother was driving each of the respective dinner wagons, blowing their horns and ringing bells. "Come and get it!" Larry called from the lead wagon.

Before Bu Zard could say another word, the animals stampeded, all running for the food wagons that had just arrived. The turkey vulture was knocked to the side as animals of all sizes hurried to get to the front of the line to eat.

Wanda kept her group out of the way and stayed close to Samuel, knowing that, right now, there was safety in being near the big gator. The other animals ran on the opposite side of the road to avoid him.

“Wanda,” Samuel said. “Before you make a final decision about leaving the march, have some dinner. Take the children over with the group and eat. Then we can discuss options. It has been a long day and we’re all tired.”

Chapter 14
A Gang of Coyotes

Many miles to the north of Bu Zard and his troubled Animal March, Victor stood alone at the center of a snarling pack of coyotes. Maurice sat above the group in a heavily leafed magnolia tree, watching the deer who was engaged in a stare-down with the leader. Maurice had jumped into the tree the moment he had sensed trouble. Now all he could do was watch.

"And so my friend, we find ourselves in a bit of dilemma. Don't you agree?" said the smug coyote leader.

Victor snorted. "Nothing that can't be worked out, I'm sure."

Earlier in the day, Victor and Maurice had found a passage underneath the mega highway dividing the state—a concrete tunnel that had been thoughtfully placed by the builder of the road for animals to use. Maurice had been helpful in getting them through the more treacherous areas of their journey across central Florida. The two had quickly moved to the north side of I-4, traveling many miles in a short time. Victor had actually asked Maurice's advice on two different occasions.

They had continued north for several hours, the terrain changing with the miles. They passed through orange groves and detoured around large freshwater lakes. Instead of the flat coastal lowlands of South Florida, the center of the state lay before them with rolling hills and a heavy congestion of both traffic and people. To avoid the crowds, the two animals decided to detour through a wooded area that would take them farther east but eventually to the Ocala National Forest.

This proved to be a mistake. When they trespassed into the coyote's territory, a gang quickly surrounded them. Maurice escaped by jumping into the closest tree and now watched as Victor faced the coyote pack alone. The leader inched closer and closer to the buck.

"I have no grievance with you," said Victor. "I am on a mission for a friend."

"Yes, yes," said the coyote. "We know all about the crazy bear. For us, he has been a blessing. You know, all the wildlife officers are trying to capture him, leaving us in control of the woods and forest. So you see, we would rather you *not* help your friend. You understand, don't you?"

Maurice watched the wily coyote carefully, while also checking out the others. He was fairly sure Victor could jump this group. But what was waiting outside the circle—in the woods? He noticed the bushes moving. From where he sat, he could make out shadowy figures lurking behind the wax myrtles that grew wild in the forest.

"I must rejoin our group, the one that is trying to reach out to the people of the state to help us protect and clean up our water. This might also be a benefit for you," Victor said with great conviction.

"Oh, yes. A noble cause, I am sure. But my sources tell me your group is still in the Everglades. There seems to be some confusion about which way is north." The coyote laughed at his own comment and the others joined him.

"Enough!" shouted the coyote. The laughing immediately stopped. "You have presented me with several problems, Mr. Deer. You have entered our territory without permission. If we let you pass through, others will want the same privilege. You understand, don't you?"

Maurice watched Victor's movements in the center of the circling coyotes. The deer glanced up into the trees. Victor was looking for him, but the cat remained still and quiet. He couldn't let the coyotes know he had stayed close by if he wanted to help the deer.

"Don't bother looking for that cowardly cat," the leader of the coyotes said. "He is long gone by now. We have seen him before. He is saving his own skin. Something *you* should have thought about before entering our woods without permission."

The coyotes closed the circle tighter around Victor. Their eyes narrowed and their teeth were bared. Drool and foam dripped from the corners of their mouths.

Victor looked for an escape, but seeing none, he lowered his head ready to do battle. His antlers were his only weapon.

Maurice saw his opportunity and sprang from his perch, dropping from the tree limb directly onto the back of the leader. With all claws extended, Maurice latched onto the coyote.

"Run, Victor! Run!" he screamed before he plunged his teeth into the coyote.

But Victor didn't run. He charged into the middle of the pack, lifting the dog-like creatures into the air with his antlers and slamming them back down to the ground. The coyotes that met with Victor's antlers jumped up from the ground and ran into the woods squealing.

Maurice's claws were stuck through the coyote's skin and wiry, coarse hair. The coyote tried to fling him off. They spun in circles and Maurice felt himself losing his grip bit by bit. Before he could deepen his hold on the coyote leader, he was sent flying through the air. He slammed into a tree.

Maurice was stunned and could not make himself get up. The coyote approached with fangs bared.

From behind Maurice's attacker came a flurry of movement. Victor lowered his head and ran at top speed toward the coyote leader. The buck speared the coyote and slung him into the bushes. The animal squealed and howled with pain.

When the remaining pack saw their leader thrown like a rag, they scattered quickly.

Maurice jumped from beside the tree and took off into the underbrush of the woods, choosing the opposite direction of the fleeing coyotes. Victor was right behind him.

Chapter 15

Hopefully, This is Not a Mistake

Bu Zard's group had a very nice afternoon. Bu Zard and Benson found a road that would take them north and they had the animals back on track after marching in circles most of the morning. The Croc Brothers' food had given everyone a needed energy boost and, once their stomachs were filled, they were able to focus on the *mission* again. They marched for several more hours before settling in for the night. The first evening under the stars was going well—for almost everyone

Bu Zard was noticeably on edge and spent a lot of time pacing the borders of their camp. *Right now would be a good time to call this quits*, he thought over and over. The walk was off-schedule and on the wrong road. The opossum, T.J., was supposedly meeting with humans in the woods and for some reason, according to those young animals, wanted to cause them harm. Benson and Samuel had searched for the opossum, but he was nowhere to be found.

Bu Zard had nearly made a humongous fool of himself today because he had believed the young ones' stories. Should he believe everything the children had told him? Why would the opossum want to stop them? The children could have heard everything wrong, couldn't they?

Frieda found Bu Zard on the outskirts of their encampment. “Hey, what are you doing? Why aren't you with the other animals?” she asked.

“I've made a mistake, Frieda. I don't know why I thought I could do this. The animals are going to hate me. I'll be the laughing stock of the Everglades.”

“What mistake, Bu Zard?” asked Frieda. “You said you were going to lead the animals to Tallahassee. You said you wanted to make the state aware of our problems back home, so where is the mistake? Are you not doing this?”

“Well, yeah,” said Bu Zard.

“Remember, the animals are here because they want to save their homes and make the Everglades a safer place, not because you asked them to come.”

“You’ve forgotten. A lot of them are here because I started that rumor about homes being built in the Everglades.”

“No, I didn’t forget and you are going to have to straighten that out sooner than later. But all of the animals here want changes to be made.” Frieda turned to head back to the group. She waved a wing at Bu Zard along with a smile of encouragement. “Come on, Bu Zard. The animals are telling haunted swamp stories. You know how you love those.”

Bu Zard looked across the field at the party that was going on and the number of animals involved. “You know, Frieda, you’re a smart bird. I just hope the animals think the way you do.”

“Frieda, you’re a smart bird.”

The adults can handle it

On the other side of the campground from Bu Zard, Desta sat with Tony, Sophie, and their Mom.

"Mom," said Tony, "we can't leave the walk. Dad's depending on us. We said we would meet him in Tallahassee. Please, please, please, let's stay."

"We'll see," was all she said.

The story of the man and opossum had circulated among the animals. But instead of the animals being frightened, they seemed unconcerned about the situation.

"Bring 'em on," a white-tailed hawk was overheard saying to his buddies. "Let them try to attack from the air. We'll show them who rules the sky."

Desta was worried and she made sure to let Tony know before they went to sleep that night.

"We've got to stay focused on this march and keep our ears open," Desta whispered to Tony. "We might find out more about the opossum and the man."

"I know, but we have to be careful," replied Tony. "I don't want to scare my mom. She'll want to go home."

"Why do you think the opossum is trying to stop the march? What will he gain by the Everglades being destroyed?" asked Desta.

"Shhhhh," Sophie whispered. "It's not our problem. Let the adults handle it."

The adults, thought Desta, *are not paying attention*. And that was the problem. She knew that Bu Zard and Samuel had too many other matters to attend to. The opossum would be the least of their worries. She and Tony would have to stay alert and warn the animals if an emergency arose. She pulled her head into her shell and prepared to sleep for the night.

Chapter 16

Smile! We're on Television

The second morning of the walk dawned without any new problems for Bu Zard. He looked up at the beautiful blue sky with renewed optimism.

The water birds did their morning bathing in the long canal that ran along the back side of the field while, several hundred feet down the waterway, the reptiles and amphibians swam laps back and forth with the Croc Brothers leading the way.

"Just getting a bit of morning exercise," Larry called out cheerily to Bu Zard who had come down to inquire about breakfast.

The Miami flamingos found that they had fans within the Animal March and were developing a following among the youth. At the moment, a group of wide-eyed foxes clamored for the attention of the divas. The pink birds told stories of the celebrities and sports stars they knew and had been photographed with.

They were so involved in telling their stories that they were late for breakfast and the food wagons had to be re-opened, delaying the animals for a full hour and causing Samuel to become agitated.

Bu Zard watched the alligator's large tail swish back and forth.

"Girls, girls, we have to get a move on. We should have been on the road an hour ago," Bu Zard told the flamingos. "We're cutting things close as it is. The legislature waits for no one, not even you beauties."

The flamingos giggled at Bu Zard's flattery. They finished breakfast and made their way to the front of the march where Samuel and Frieda waited impatiently. As the animals prepared to leave the field, the first television camera crews pulled off the road and parked their trucks.

Bu Zard walked over to Samuel and raised his wings with a shrug. "It will just take a minute, Samuel. I promise."

Each of the trucks had the name of their particular TV station written down both sides and came equipped with a large satellite dish.

Reporters jumped from the trucks with their microphones and headed toward the animals waiting in the field.

Any thoughts about getting on the road early were quickly abandoned. Their new goal was to be on the five o'clock news.

"This is Sam McDonald of WBRD news, reporting from just north of the Everglades where you can see this very large group of animals gathered behind me," said a reporter for a Miami station. Then, shouting because the noise level was increasing, he continued. "The animals have left the Everglades, a place that many of their families have called home for eons. They have left the safety of the 'Glades to march to the Capitol of Florida, many not knowing if they will ever see their homes again."

The reporter paused so the station anchor could respond from the news studio. "But, Sam, why would they do this? Have you learned anything from the animals? Is this a threat to the people of the state? Are they saying what they want from the Governor?"

"Yes, Katie, they are talking. I have personally spoken to the group's coordinators. They are demanding that the water be cleaned up. They want all future developments to be highly regulated in the immediate vicinity of the water flowing to the Everglades. This includes large-scale farming, Katie. Katie, can you hear me? As you can see—"

The flamingos had moved in behind the reporter, blowing kisses and waving at the camera man. Rome yelled and waved, while Kandee tried to grab the microphone. "We just want to tell everyone back home in Miami, hello and we love you!"

"Hi, Mama! We're on TV," yelled Lola, while adjusting her tiara.

"As you can see, Katie," continued the correspondent, "others from around the state have joined in on this historic march. We will keep you informed of the status of the march and update you throughout the day. This is the Miami WBRD news team, reporting from somewhere near Lake Okeechobee." The reporter could be seen by the viewers at home, fighting off the flamingos as they grabbed for the microphone he held tight in his hand.

Across the field, a Wolf News camera man and reporter attempted to get photographs of the Croc Brothers waving their signs. At least five stations interviewed the animals while doing live news reports.

Bu Zard and Frieda ran from group to group to make sure the reporters were getting the record straight.

"Yes, our plan is to march across this state. We are asking the people and lawmakers to help save the Everglades," Bu Zard said with as much dignity as he could muster. "We are the *United Species of Animals*, and we are asking that our homes be protected. We cannot afford to forget how important this ecosystem called the Everglades is to the surrounding systems."

Samuel sat quietly to the side, waiting patiently and watching the sun rise higher and higher in the sky. For the second day in a row, the animals were getting a late start. The legislators would not stay in Tallahassee forever. The animals still had a long way to go to get to the Capitol and make their voices heard.

Time for plan B

Many miles away, in room 132 of the Palms Motel, a TV blared with the morning news report.

"This is the Miami WBRD news team, reporting from somewhere near Lake Okeechobee."

"Turn it off," said the man as he straightened his tie in the mirror and placed his hat on his head. "Turn it off, I've heard enough. I'll take care of this. The animals need something to do besides clog up traffic."

The opossum looked across the room at the boar sitting quietly by the window. Then he walked over to shut the TV off, rolling his eyes at the man as he did.

Chapter 17

News of the Bear

While the Animal March was getting a slow start to the day, Victor and Maurice had made great time. They were working their way north and had just arrived at the edge of the Ocala National Forest.

It was almost noon. The sun was hot and the two animals were thirsty. They searched until they found a lake where they could get a drink and rest from their long run.

Instead of pretending that Maurice did not exist, Victor waited on him to catch up. Being thrown into the tree by the leader of the coyotes had knocked the breath from the bobcat. It was the adrenalin pumping through his body that got Maurice out of the woods fast, but the run-in with the vicious animals had taken its toll and he was tired.

"Let's stop," said Victor. "I need to rest."

Maurice looked over at the big buck and smiled. "I'm okay."

"No, let's stop. You said we were getting close to Ocala and we're going to need all our strength before going after Jason. Let's rest."

Maurice was aware that Victor could run all day, but for himself, he could use a little recovery time and he appreciated the gesture by the buck, especially since Victor had made it clear he did not want to be slowed down.

Maurice found a soft clump of tall grass and scrabbled around in it until he had arranged himself a comfortable spot in the middle. After circling several times, he dropped down in his newly made bed and watched Victor.

Since their arrival at the lake, Victor had seemed distracted, often staring absent-mindedly into the distance.

"Why *did* you do this, Victor?" asked Maurice. "Take on this job, I mean. You could be with your family right now. But instead, here we are looking for a bear that means . . . what to you?"

"I have my reasons," said Victor. "I'm not going to talk about it. We've got other things to take care of."

Maurice watched the buck for a moment. Then he let the matter drop. He did not want to go back to the way things were before Victor began treating him as an equal.

"Look around, Maurice," said Victor after they had rested a bit. "We need to find an animal that can give us information about Jason. I'm sure the bear is the topic of the forest as well as the city."

Finding an animal was not hard, but finding one that would tell them anything about Jason took a while. The animals were naturally suspicious of strangers in the forest. They hid as soon as Maurice arrived. Finally, Maurice found a bobwhite that would talk.

"Bobwhite!" said the bird, displaying the bobwhites' habit of repeatedly calling their name over and over. "Bobwhite! We haven't seen the bear for several weeks. Bobwhite! Bobwhite!

Not since he found a group of campers around his den in the middle of the woods. Bobwhite! He was mad. I think he said if people were going to come into his home and crowd him, he would just go visit theirs. Bobwhite! That's the last we've seen of him. Bobwhite! Bobwhite!" The bird finished and flew away to a clump of bushes, calling out his name as he went.

"Well, it looks like we'll have to go into the city of Ocala," Maurice told Victor. "I was hoping he would return to the forest on his own. I'm not looking forward to going into populated areas with you and that rack on your head."

"Maybe we can use some camouflage," suggested the deer. "Disguise ourselves and blend in. There's a possibility I might lose these antlers before we get there. I usually shed them by now, to make room for a larger set."

Maurice looked at the buck and shook his head back and forth. "Yeah, right, blend in. If we hang your antlers on some hunter's wall you might blend in, but other than that . . . " The cat's voice faded away as he thought about the situation. "I don't know. Let me think about it."

Camouflaging Victor was not the only problem they faced. Convincing the bear to follow them to Tallahassee was not going to be easy. Jason was being hunted, and he was obviously in a very bad mood. From what Victor and Maurice had been told, Jason had lost multiple homes to invading humans. To top it all off, Jason was not the only animal that would be in trouble if he was caught in the city. Humans were fine when trespassing around the homes of the animals. But a bear, a bobcat, and a large buck having a meeting in a living room would likely put all three of them in danger of being arrested by the wildlife control officers.

The two animals began to make their plans for sneaking into the city.

Chapter 18
Time to Pick Up the Pace

Bu Zard and the flamingos were once again at the front of the Animal March, leading the animals toward Tallahassee. The leisurely pace of the day before had been replaced with a lot more hustle, due in part to the presence of Samuel who was currently doing his mouth exercises.

It had not gone unnoticed by Bu Zard that the big gator was within snipping range of the four divas and had snapped his mouth shut several times with such ferocity that a few pink tail feathers had become dislodged from the flamingos' behinds and now clung to the side of Samuel's mouth.

"Let's pick it up, girls," Bu Zard had said more than once in the last half hour.

While the four birds were not commenting on Samuel's proximity to their backsides, their quickened pace, as well as their newly acquired positive attitudes, were indications that they were aware of Samuel's unspoken direction.

Bu Zard, on the other hand, didn't feel as threatened by Samuel. The vulture couldn't stop talking about their morning press conference. Acting giddy and forgetting how important it was to keep up a fast pace, he turned to Samuel and gave the alligator a wink.

"Oh, yeah, now we have their attention. The press loves us," Bu Zard said. Then he turned his attention to the flamingos. "We'll be the main topic on the news all day. Everyone will know we're marching to the Capitol of Florida. Everyone! Isn't that right, girls?"

The pink flamingos wholeheartedly agreed and, for hours, walked along reliving every word that had been said. Bu Zard thought he presented himself as profound and serious, while the divas thought they appeared sophisticated and beautiful.

Bu Zard was well aware that Frieda was annoyed. He could tell by the way she stomped along beside him, but he could not stop from reliving the press conference. It had been too exciting.

"Did you see how the camera man zoomed in on my face?" asked Kandee.

"Oh, no, I missed that," Bu Zard replied. "I was doing multiple interviews. Did you notice how many stations were trying to get my statement? There was actually a shoving match between the reporters from Wolf News station and WCNB."

Before he finished his sentence, Frieda threw up her wings in disgust and stomped off, complaining about the size of the egos walking beside her. The last thing Bu Zard heard her say as she walked away was that her feet were burning and she'd rather be strangled by a boa constrictor than spend another second with the pink fluffs.

It is definitely a plane

The hot asphalt of the highway, heated by the afternoon sun, was beginning to bother and cause discomfort for many of the animals. Desta and her friends moved to the grassy right-of-way because of Desta's sore feet, which were webbed and more agreeable to a pond than a highway. Desta watched the blue heron, Frieda, huffing and puffing as she made her way to the roadside.

"Ow, ow, ouch," Frieda said while hopping across the pavement.

"Come and march with us," said Wanda. "I can't help but notice there is no love lost between you and the flamingos."

"Thank you," said Frieda. "I'd love some actual adult conversation."

"I can't promise that," said Wanda looking around at the young ones.

"Flying is so much easier," Frieda told Wanda. "How do you ever do it? Walk everywhere, I mean."

Wanda did not get a chance to answer. Since the early morning news reports had aired on national television, the highway had become rather crowded with curious onlookers. A new line of cars approached the group. And the animals, while waving their signs, moved to the side of the road to allow them room to pass.

Above the animals, a small plane flew in close. The closer it came, the lower it flew. As soon as it passed the animals, it climbed high into the sky.

Frieda watched the plane as it circled at a higher altitude then flew off toward the east.

"I don't like all the attention we're getting," she told Wanda. "I don't know why Bu Zard had to alert the country to the fact we're making this crazy trip. I just don't think we're safe."

"I believe that was the second time that plane has flown over us this morning," said Wanda.

"Third," said Tony and Sophie together.

"Third," echoed Desta. "Each time it comes in lower."

"Do you think Bu Zard is paying attention to this?" Frieda asked her new friends. "I think not. I think Bu Zard is more concerned about being on the five o'clock news with his pink friends, than with the safety of our group."

The animals watched the plane until it disappeared from sight.

"Well, it's gone," said Wanda. "I'm sure it's just another group trying to get a look at us."

Desta looked over at Tony, who was still staring at the sky even though the plane was long gone.

"Are you thinking what I'm thinking?" asked Desta.

"Hit them from the air," said Tony, keeping his voice low so his mother and Frieda could not hear him. "They said they would hit us from the air."

"What could they possibly do with that small plane?" asked Desta. "Land on top of us?"

As if to answer the question, the small plane returned, coming in at treetop level and taking the animals by surprise. This time, Bu Zard took notice, as did Samuel and the rest of the animals.

"Take cover," Bu Zard yelled. "Incoming."

But the plane was almost upon them, flying straight above the center line of the road and aiming at the group of animals.

Desta spotted a man leaning out of the open door of the plane; his bright blue tie with yellow half-moons blew in the wind. The opossum standing beside him handed a long cylinder to the man who took aim at the crowd.

The animals tried to scatter—but too late. The man pushed the plunger at the end of the cylinder and a packet shot out. Then he turned and took the next cylinder handed to him. After half a dozen packages were shot from the cylinders, the small plane pulled up and climbed, disappearing over the trees as quickly as it had appeared.

Desta, Tony, and Sophie watched, unable to move out of the way, as the packages fell through the air toward them. Small parachutes popped out of the top of each package and opened, slowing the descent to the ground. When the first package finally reached the ground, it was only a few feet in front of them.

The sides split open, revealing the contents of the brown and white paper-wrapped bundle.

The entire event happened in less than a minute. One after another, parachutes brought their cargo to the ground, landing amidst the animals. At first, none of the animals moved. Then they all moved at once.

Desta and Tony were the first to reach one of the bundles over the protests of Wanda who was trying hard to get around the animals separating her from her children.

"Stop, don't touch it!" screeched Bu Zard flying into the middle of the circle. "Get back! We don't know what's in those!"

Then, throwing himself on top of the package, Bu Zard covered his head with his wings and held his breath. The weight of Bu Zard, landing with a plop in the middle of the brown bundle, sent pieces of paper from the package into the air. With a poof, the paper fell among the animals.

Frieda screamed and took off in flight, circling above the vulture, who was being uncharacteristically heroic.

The flamingos followed Frieda, circling above the animals.

"Enough, enough," cried Lola. "Let's go, girls. Time to find some *famous* friends to hang out with. I think the Miami Heat basketball team is playing the Orlando Magic. We're close to Orlando, and with *all* our connections, I'm sure *we* can get good tickets."

Bu Zard could only watch as the flamingos made one last circle and flew away.

"It's just a brochure," said Desta, who sat reading from one on the ground nearest her. "The people of the state of Florida invite you to a free, all-expense paid vacation to Hurricane Hamlet. Enjoy six nights and seven days at the all-inclusive resort, Maki Maki, located within Hurricane Hamlet Water Park."

The animals make a circle around the turtle. Those that had run into the woods when the plane appeared now returned along with some of the birds that had flown away.

Desta flipped the brochure over and continued reading on the back side. "Hurricane Hamlet, located on the outskirts of beautiful Orlando, Florida, includes a one hundred-acre water park. Enjoy lazy days floating on the two-mile river. Ride the rapids on a mile-long, authentic whitewater river adventure or take turns on the famous hurricane slides." Desta paused and looked up at the animals.

"Go on, keep reading," said Betty, the wood stork.

"The first four hundred animals through the gates will be eligible to win a Caribbean cruise. Limited time offer," read Desta.

"Stop reading right there," said Bu Zard. "We don't have time for this now. We can go there on the way *back* from Tallahassee. Remember, we have a mission to get to Tallahassee while the lawmakers are meeting. We have to get our water cleaned up and save our homes first."

"But the people of Florida invited us," said Betty. "That must mean something."

"Well, we certainly can't insult the people of the state," said a beaver.

"Of course, we can't," said Betty. "After all, we are trying to get their help to save our homes. I think this is a nice gesture."

"But, but," Bu Zard stammered. "You don't really believe the people of the state invited us, do you? Why would they do this?"

"It's in writing, so they must have," said a Croc Brother.

Desta looked around at the animals and back to Bu Zard.

A white-tailed hawk named Hal interrupted Bu Zard with a simple question to Desta. "What is the limited time the offer is talking about?"

"It's in the fine print," said Desta. "Let me see. No cash value, entire value must be used in one visit, cannot be combined with any other promotion or offer, brochure is the ticket. Hmmmm, let me see. Yes, here it is. This offer is good for twenty-four hours from . . . uuuuhhh . . . today."

Chapter 19

A Chance of a Lifetime

Bu Zard threw up his wings, and then flapped them up and down, trying to get the attention of the animals. The offer on the brochure was causing a gigantic uproar. The vulture couldn't believe that there was talk of actually abandoning their march to the Capitol. He flapped his wings harder and blew his whistle.

The crowd didn't pay attention to the vulture.

"All expenses paid!"

"It's the chance of a lifetime!"

"The people from the state invited us."

"Please, Mama! Can we go?"

From all areas of the crowd, every animal was excited.

"No, no, we can't do it," shouted Bu Zard. "We have to get to the Capitol before the session ends. We must speak to our representatives in the legislature. Stay focused, everyone. Please listen to me!"

Bu Zard's pleas were to no avail. He watched as the Croc Brothers led the animals in the Macarena line dance.

Bu Zard blew his whistle and flew in circles over the animals, but succeeded in getting the attention of only Wanda and Samuel.

Samuel roared. The animals quieted themselves immediately. Samuel nodded at Bu Zard to talk to the animals. The vulture landed beside the alligator and tried again to convince the animals to stay with the march.

"This is just a diabolical plan to stop us from going to the Capitol and meeting with our representatives in the legislature," Bu Zard told the group.

"Why would anyone develop a diabolical anything that involved us?" asked a barred owl.

"Probably to save the development they wish to build in the Everglades," Wanda answered.

"No, can't be that," said Bu Zard, without thinking about the implications of his words.

"What do you mean it can't be that?" asked Wanda.

"I mean, I mean." Bu Zard stopped, he was stuck. He had lied about the development of homes deep in the Everglades, so, of course, it couldn't be that. But how could he tell them without giving away his lie? "Well, just that the development was not a done deal. It's probably about cleaning the water up," he said quickly in hopes he could skip right past his lie.

The animals were completely quiet for three seconds. Then an animal from the back shouted, "Water park!" and the Croc Brothers started their dance again.

Bu Zard could only try to move out of the way as most of the group took off in the direction of Hurricane Hamlet.

A lone cameraman from Wolf News had been given a tip to be in the area at the exact time the plane flew over. He caught the stampede on video and then hurried off to get the film ready for the five o'clock news. The animals had abandoned the march.

The loss of trust

Bu Zard was knocked to the ground by the sudden stampede of animals. Finally, after a few frightening moments, he got to his feet and shook off the dirt and debris from the road. He turned to look at the remainder of the marchers that had stayed behind.

"Really, really?" he said in disbelief. "Just throw out a few freebies and the entire mission is abandoned?"

Desta stuck her head out of her shell. It seemed the safest place for her when the animals stampeded. She quickly jerked her head back into the shell as a group of frogs and toads hopped by. When she felt like the coast was finally clear, Desta pushed her head out of her shell once again and turned in a circle.

She had watched Bu Zard as he had picked himself up off the road and shook the sand and gravel from his feathers. Nearby, Wanda, and behind her, Tony and Sophie, stood very close to Samuel. The turtle finished looking around and let out a long sigh. "It looks like we're the only ones left," she said aloud.

Benson and Della circled, then landed beside Bu Zard. "They're all headed toward the water park," Benson said. "If they'd been moving like that to start with, we would be halfway to Tallahassee."

"Bu Zard," a voice called from above.

The animals looked up and watched Frieda flying in circles overhead.

"Bu Zard, I don't think many animals are going to go with us," she said as she landed on the ground beside the turkey vulture.

Desta crawled over to her friends. "Well, I guess that turned out differently than we thought."

Bu Zard shook his red head back and forth and said, "But why? Why would anyone give us free passes to a water park?"

"Because we weren't supposed to make it to Tallahassee," said Desta. "The opossum didn't want us to go. The man in the blue tie didn't want us to go. They must have a reason."

Samuel slowly moved his tail back and forth. "Bu Zard, what were you talking about a moment ago? When you said it's not a done deal? We *are* asking the state to save our homes," he said. "To do that, they'll have to make changes that will affect a lot of business owners and homeowners. It'll also have a negative impact on the ten thousand homes that are supposed to be built. The developer could be angry with us for trying to stop the project."

"But that's not true." Bu Zard knew he had to tell them the truth.

All the animals turned to look at him.

"What's not true?" asked Samuel.

"Well, ummm . . . " It was time for him to come clean. "It was really only twenty-five hundred houses," he admitted. "I mean, originally, when I started the rumor."

"Why would you start a rumor?" Wanda stammered.

"*Tch, tch, tch*," Frieda clucked a few times.

Bu Zard was grateful that all she did was cluck. "It's going to happen. The Everglades are going to be overrun with homes—someday. I just thought we shouldn't wait until it's too late. We have to act now while we can do something."

"What about trust, Bu Zard?" asked Benson. "Isn't that important?"

Bu Zard looked from face to face of the remaining animals. He knew he'd messed up, big time. He'd lost all the ground gained in winning their trust. Bu Zard's wings hung limply by his side and he dropped his head.

Samuel hadn't said a word, but his tail moved back and forth, and he snapped his mouth open and closed, obviously speechless.

"I'm sorry," Bu Zard said.

Wanda wasn't having any of it. "You brought my children and me out into a risky situation for a 'what if'?"

"Wanda, I . . . "

"Don't Wanda me."

Desta tapped Bu Zard's leg, but he was too embarrassed to look down. So she crawled over to Tony and Sophie, and in the loudest voice she could muster said, "We still don't know why the opossum and the man in the tie wanted to turn us around and why they want to relocate us." Then, without taking a breath, she continued. "But most of all, we don't know *why* they wanted the animals to go to the water park." The little turtle remembered the words of the big leatherback turtle from the first meeting they'd attended. "Animals outside the Everglades are being affected. Something bad is definitely happening," she said.

The adults stopped arguing. The little turtle had made a good point.

"Well, what're we going to do?" Bu Zard asked the small group surrounding him. The turkey vulture was at a loss. All of his hard work, the weeks of planning, everything gone in the blink of an eye. The vulture dropped his head again.

"Let's go get them," said Wanda. "We're going to go get those animals. Tell them the truth and let them make a decision based on facts."

Tony and Sophie looked at their mom in complete surprise.

The doe continued talking. "Let's go to the park and tell them what's going on. We'll explain what we *think* the motive is behind this vacation, and we can at least warn them about the man with the tie and the opossum."

Bu Zard perked up. "That's a great idea. If we can get just half of them to continue, maybe we can still make it in time to meet with the legislature."

Wanda shook her head and snorted. "I doubt that's going to happen. But the animals deserve to hear the truth."

"It's a free week-long pass, Mom," said Tony. "Do you really think we can get them to leave a water park that's all fun and games?"

"Well, we can try," said Bu Zard. "We have to try. I don't trust either one of those two, the man with the tie or the opossum. We have to at least go there and make sure the animals are safe. We have no idea what really might be waiting for them at the park. We don't know what they mean by relocation."

"Della and I will fly ahead and see if we can get any of them to speak with us," said Benson. The two eagles took off and headed in the direction the other animals had gone.

Samuel's tail still twitched back and forth, and his disappointment was evident when he looked at Bu Zard. "I'll go and help you get the animals from the park," he said. "Then I'm going back to the Everglades."

Bu Zard dropped his wings, letting them droop into the dirt. "I'm sorry, Samuel. I know I let you down."

Frieda stood beside her friend and watched Samuel crawl away.

"At least we'll move faster without those pink fuzz balls with us," Frieda said, hoping the thought would cheer Bu Zard up as much as it did her.

Chapter 20
Where's the Bear?

In the middle of downtown Ocala, Victor stood looking at Maurice and shaking his head. "Sorry, Maurice, not going to do it. I realize you saved my life and everything, but sorry, I'm not going to dress up as a street advertisement for Mama Sue's Pizzeria."

The two animals had made it this far in their search for the wayward bear. But now, Maurice needed to use his stealth abilities to track the bear inside the city limits. Victor was just too big and too obvious to go along.

"But, Vic, buddy, this is the perfect disguise. Just put these signs over your head that direct traffic to Mama Sue's Pizzeria. Anytime someone looks at you, you just stand up on your back legs and ring this bell. Everyone will think you're selling pizza in one of those stupid costumes people wear to get attention," Maurice said, with a pleading tone.

"Think again, Maurice," Victor said. "*Stupid* costume is your clue."

"You got a better idea?" asked Maurice. "Because, if you do, I'm listening. You know they shoot deer around here, don't you?"

Thirty minutes later, Victor stood at the corner of Highway 441 and Pine Street in Ocala with a large cardboard sign hanging from his neck. The front read MAMA SUE'S PIZZERIA and the back had PIZZA BY THE SLICE $2.00. The bell hanging around his neck completed his costume.

Maurice ran around the block trying to catch the scent of the black bear. The sooner he found Jason, the sooner he and Victor could get out of town. They were in as much danger of being arrested by wildlife control as Jason was. Maurice only traveled a few blocks when he ran into a good source of information on the bear.

An old city raccoon sifted through garbage from a can he had knocked over behind Wong Lee's Chinese Restaurant. He was in no mood to share the egg rolls left over from the previous night's all-you-can-eat buffet. When Maurice poked his head around the corner, the raccoon arched his back and hissed at the wildcat.

"Hey, man. It's cool. I'm not after your wontons. I just need a little information. You okay with that? I'm just going to stand right here," said Maurice. "Look, paws in the air, no funny business. I need to know if you've seen a bear. He goes by the name of Jason. He's big, black, about yea high. Probably getting into trouble. Does any of this ring a bell?"

The raccoon took a bite of an egg roll and chewed slowly, keeping one eye on the bobcat and the other eye on his food. Finally, after a couple of bites, he answered Maurice.

"Yeah, I've seen him, 'bout ten blocks north of here," the raccoon said with a mouthful of egg roll. "Over off Pots Street. Had some lady screaming first thing this morning. I heard she found him in the pantry. Anyway, police and wildlife control officers are all over the place. That bear is making it hard for the rest of us around here. They've been picking up a lot of city animals in their sweeps for the bear. A homeless dog isn't safe around here right now."

The raccoon would have said more, but right at that moment, Wong Lee came out of the restaurant with another bag of garbage. When he saw the raccoon, the bobcat, and the knocked-over trashcan in the alley, his eyes narrowed and he charged at the two animals.

Maurice barely missed being hit by flying garbage as he sprinted out of the alley with the raccoon right behind them. Wong Lee followed for several blocks, throwing old onions and screaming at them in Chinese.

Maurice was still running when he passed Victor standing on the corner. "Ditch the sign and come on," he yelled as he ran by his friend. "I know where the bear is!"

Chapter 21

A Disturbing Sight

Bu Zard's small band of animals made it to the water park by mid-afternoon the next day. They arrived just in time to see a large limousine drive away with the Croc Brothers, their heads poking through the sunroof, wearing flowered leis and waving goodbye to Bu Zard while yelling, "Bon voyage!"

Bu Zard stared at the back of the car until it was out of sight. He turned to face the massive gates of Hurricane Hamlet Water Park. A large, overhead sign showed a picture of a small village surrounded by the image of a hurricane symbol with the name of the park in large, black letters underneath the picture. The gates were closed and a sign on the front had an arrow pointing to a row of ticket booths on the side of the gates.

A small sign read:

Closed For Private Party
Re-opening Next Week
Come Back Then

"How are we going to find the rest of the animals?" asked Bu Zard.

"How are we going to find the rest of the animals?"

“I don’t like the fence around this place,” said Samuel. “It’s pretty high.”

“I’m sure it’s to keep people out who don’t have tickets,” said Bu Zard.

“Or to keep animals in,” said Frieda.

“Well, yes, there’s always that,” said Bu Zard. “Maybe we should take a walk around this place to find other possible exits.”

“Or escape routes,” Frieda added.

Bu Zard put his wing against Frieda’s side and said, “It’ll be all right, Frieda. Just trust me on this one thing, will you?”

“I’m trying, Bu Zard. I really am, but there’s no way you can know that things will be *all right*.”

Benson and Della landed beside Bu Zard as he was laying out their options. The two birds had flown ahead in hopes of arranging a meeting between Bu Zard and the animals.

“You’ve got to see this,” said Della as soon as she landed.

“We’ve got to go to the back service gate. The situation there is disturbing,” said Benson. “It’s very disturbing. We noticed a lot of activity while we were flying the perimeter, looking for exits, so we flew in to take a closer look.”

“What is it?” asked Tony.

“You’ll have to come with us and look. We don’t know what to make of it. It just doesn’t look good and we probably don’t want them to see us.”

Bu Zard and his small group followed the bald eagles along the fence line, staying in the shadows as much as possible. On the complete opposite side of the entrance to the park, an ominous sight awaited them. Rows of large, semi-tractor trailers were lined up outside the delivery gate of Hurricane Hamlet. Each trailer had HM CONSOLIDATED ENTERPRISES painted down the side. A large half-moon was stamped into each metal door on all the truck cabs.

The trucks sat with motors running. Clouds of black smoke from the diesel billowed from the exhaust stacks attached to both sides of the cabs. The opossum could be seen standing on his hind legs at the front of the long line of trucks, talking to a few of the drivers.

"Stay back," Benson said, warning the animals before they exposed themselves to the group gathered at the gate. "We noticed them pulling in and parking about an hour ago. They've been coming steady since then."

The animals retreated quickly and hid behind a row of tanks that held chemicals for the park's water rides.

They watched the drivers return to their trucks, turn off the engines, and sit, waiting.

"What are they waiting for?" asked Frieda.

None of the animals could answer her question.

"Now what?" asked Wanda.

Desta crawled over to Bu Zard and placed her small webbed foot on his claw. She and Tony had whispered their suspicions to each other as soon as they saw the trucks.

The vulture looked down at the turtle.

"This has to be part of the relocation plan that the opossum and the man were talking about in the woods. Relocation—move somewhere else—trucks. That would make sense."

The animals began to talk all together.

Bu Zard raised his wings. "Stop! Be quiet. We need to be calm and discuss this."

The animals looked at Bu Zard and began talking again.

"Quiet!" This command came from Samuel. The animals stopped talking to stare at the alligator who continued by addressing Bu Zard. "Do you have anything in mind, Bu Zard?"

"Yes! We've got to get inside and warn the animals!"

Chapter 22
Jason's Big Mess

Maurice and Victor were a long way from the problems of the Animal March. But that didn't mean they weren't without their own difficulties. The pair had traveled down eight city blocks when they picked up Jason's trail. It wasn't hard. Not only did they pick up the bear's scent but they could see the local law enforcement that surrounded a house on West Seventh Street. The closer they got to the bear, the more they realized just how much trouble he was in; wildlife officers were everywhere. Bad publicity was only a fraction of what this bear was facing. Jason could be given the death penalty if he got caught inside a house again.

"I hope we're in time," said Maurice, "because he's certainly not being very discreet."

"This way." Victor sniffed the air and turned his head from side to side. "He's not in there. They have the wrong house."

Maurice sniffed the air. "Right," he said. "His scent is coming from the opposite direction. He's a few blocks away. He was here though and judging from all the game and wildlife control officers surrounding that house, he left a mess."

The two animals crossed Eighth Street and jumped a backyard fence to get around the hullabaloo that was happening on Seventh Street. They ran and jumped from backyard to backyard. They only made it through a few yards before a small child spotted them and screamed.

"Get down, Victor," said Maurice. "Hide those racks on your head."

Victor dropped to his front knees, lowered his head, and crawled along the fence line toward the garden gate, the tips of his antlers still visible above the wooden fence.

Maurice pulled some towels from a nearby clothesline and draped them across the buck's antlers.

"All right, that should help hide the racks," he said.

Victor nodded, agreeing with Maurice's camouflage idea. They didn't want the neighbors calling wildlife control and giving away Jason's location. At that instant, they heard a loud crash from inside the house next door.

Maurice immediately headed in that direction. Following the noise, he jumped into a dogwood tree. The flowering tree helped hide him as he walked across a limb that hung over the fence of the neighboring backyard. Once he cleared the fence, he dropped from the limb onto the ground below.

Victor checked for the child. Then he ran and jumped easily over the fence He looked very strange with the towels flying off as he sailed through mid-air.

Both animals approached the house cautiously. They could smell the bear and knew he was inside, but a lot of noise came through the open back door and they weren't sure of what they'd find.

"Let's not spook him," whispered Maurice to Victor who stood peeking around the door. "He might be one of those bears that bites first and asks questions later."

Their first glimpse was into the kitchen. A table had been pushed up against the wall and four chairs lay broken on the floor. Pots and pans were scattered everywhere. Some lay under the table and others were heaped into a pile beside the cabinet where they were once stacked. Across the kitchen, the pantry door stood open. A bag of flour was scattered on the floor along with an open container of sugar and boxes of spices. Metal cans had rolled around the kitchen when they fell off a shelf now dangling from the wall.

Another loud crash came from inside. Maurice and Victor leaned a little further into the room, hoping to see the bear.

Maurice poked Victor with his paw and nodded at the refrigerator door that stood wide open. A jug of milk lay turned over on the floor with a steady stream of white liquid running out of it and across the kitchen.

They could see the feet of the bear beneath the door and his rear end sticking out as he leaned into the refrigerator. Two large, red circles were painted on his backside, one for each time the wildlife control officers had been called in to remove the bear from someone's home or backyard.

The bear grunted and growled, struggling with something deep inside the refrigerator and unaware of the two spectators watching him from outside the kitchen door. Victor walked across the floor of the kitchen, carefully stepping over the mess the bear had made. Maurice jumped onto the counter and crossed over to the refrigerator. He gracefully leaped to the top of the appliance and looked down at the bear. He made sure to stay just out of the bear's reach.

"Jason, Jason! My man, what are you doing in there?" Maurice asked.

Jason jerked straight up, hitting his head inside the refrigerator. "What the—?"

He pulled his head out of the refrigerator and looked up at Maurice. The bear still had evidence of the broken bag of flour sticking to his black button nose and the fur on his face. In one paw, he held a fried chicken leg and, in the other, a chunk of cheese.

"Hey, you scared me. What are you doing sneaking up on me like that?" Jason said.

"A-hum." Victor cleared his throat.

Jason jerked forward and hit his head on the refrigerator again. He backed away slowly and turned around to look at Victor.

"There are two of you? What are you doing here? You know this is a dangerous neighborhood, don't you?" he said. "Someone tried to shoot me earlier today."

"And why do you think someone would try and shoot you?" asked Maurice. "I mean, besides the fact that you *are* breaking into homes and," Maurice looked around the room, "making some really big messes. This isn't going to go well with these people when they come home."

Jason shrugged, tilted his head, and met Maurice eye to eye. "I have lost three homes because of humans. I've moved and then moved again. Something just snapped," said the bear. "I'll be long gone before they even get home, something that

“Jason, Jason! My man, what are you doing in there?”

can't be said about the humans that live on top of my old dens. They are there to stay."

"Yeah, yeah, I've heard all about it," said Maurice, stopping the bear. "Problem is, Victor here promised your mother he would come get you. I thought I'd tag along and watch the fun. But this game is over. We have to get moving."

"My *mother*? I told her not to worry. I'm a big boy and I can take care of myself," said Jason. "Besides, *I'm* not ready to go anywhere yet. I'm having too much fun here." Then he took a large bite of the chicken leg.

Victor walked over to the door and lifted his head, smelling the air. "I don't think you have a choice, Jason," he said. "They're bringing in the dogs." As if to prove his point, a dog howled in the distance. Victor turned back to Maurice. "Let's go. We'll all be caught if we don't start moving."

"We've got a little time," said Jason. "I went to two other houses and dumped flour all over the place before I came to this one. That should clog up the dogs' sinuses for a while."

The howling from the dogs started again, but this time they were much closer.

Maurice jumped from the refrigerator down to the floor, rushing past Jason and onto the back porch.

"Closing in," he said. "These dogs are smart, Jason. They've skipped the last house and are on the way. Follow me. We only have a few minutes."

The three animals rushed out of the house and into the backyard. Maurice jumped onto the dogwood branch and motioned for Jason to follow. Victor jumped the fence landing once again in the yard with the little girl.

"I'll lead them away from you to give you time to get the bear out of town," Victor yelled to the bobcat.

"Go, Victor," said Maurice. "We'll meet you in Gulf Hammock later."

"Where in Gulf Hammock?" asked Victor.

"Cypress Point. You'll have to ask an animal where it is when you get there! Climb, Jason! Move it, Victor. I can see the dogs. They're almost here!"

Maurice watched Victor jump the fences, only seconds in front of the dogs and wildlife control officers that had found their way to Jason's big mess.

Chapter 23
Inside Hurricane Hamlet

Bu Zard jumped up and down in front of the ticket booth located near the front gate of Hurricane Hamlet. Frieda and Desta looked for help while Samuel, Wanda, and her fawns watched the vulture trying to get them into the park. But so far, Bu Zard hadn't found anyone or any animal to help. He flapped his wings trying to lift himself high enough to see inside the booth. Unfortunately, a shade was pulled down and a cardboard sign said CLOSED.

It took several minutes, but finally Frieda located a ticket master in the next to the last booth. The shade covering the window was partially closed, but a pair of tusks was partly visible at the bottom of the window.

"Park's closed," said the voice from inside. "Private party's here for the rest of the week."

"We have these," Bu Zard told the ticket master and stuffed the brochures that had been dropped from the plane under the glass of the ticket office.

The ticket master fumbled around for a moment before raising the shade a tiny bit. He leaned down far enough for the animals to see his snout.

"Well, I guess you're within the twenty-four hour time period. But you're too late to be entered into the drawing for the Caribbean cruise. More than four hundred animals were in front of you. We had the drawing about thirty minutes ago. A trio of singing and dancing crocodiles won," the ticket master said. "Pretty sure they left in a private limousine for Port Canaveral."

Bu Zard and Frieda exchanged glances. Considering what the animals had just witnessed outside the park with the trucks, the thought of the Croc Brothers waving goodbye from the back of the limousine was disconcerting.

"They left in a vehicle!" Frieda whispered.

"*Shhh!* Don't say anything. Just get the tickets," Bu Zard whispered back.

Frieda reached the tip of her wing into the small opening under the ticket booth window and took the ID tags that had GUEST stamped in bold on the front.

"How do we get in?" Bu Zard asked.

"Please step forward," said the ticket master. "I'll have the gates unlocked."

This time Bu Zard and Frieda looked at each other with wide-eyed alarm. Bu Zard swallowed hard to get the lump in his throat to move down.

"Did he say unlocked?" asked Frieda. "*Tch, tch, tch,* that's not good, not good at all. We're going to be locked in and never get out of this place. I'll never see the Everglades again. I'm not going in."

"Miss Frieda," said Desta. The turtle called Frieda's name several times before she got her attention. "Miss Frieda, you do have wings. You can always fly out if you want to."

Bu Zard shook his head back and forth. "Don't worry so much, Frieda. We'll get out," he told her. But he had to swallow again to keep the fear from rising in his throat. He and Frieda could fly out, but the rest of his group most definitely could *not* fly.

"Are you sure you want to take the young ones in?" Bu Zard said to Wanda and Samuel. "It might be a lot harder for you to get out of the park if we get locked in."

Neither Wanda nor Samuel had a chance to answer. A buzzing sound came from the other side of the fence and an electronic gate swung open. The animals could finally see inside the fence.

Thick, tropical foliage blocked the view of the park that lay behind it. But what the animals could see caused the small group to stop, mouths and beaks dropping open. Red and yellow flowers bloomed along the sides of the walkway that led to a wide wooden bridge. A small river ran under the wooden structure, and the group could see the animals as they traveled along the river. Some were in rubber tubes, while others swam and floated on the slow-moving river.

Before Wanda could stop them, Tony and Sophie darted inside the gates and headed for the river.

The grown-ups' only choice was to follow the two children into the park. Desta walked cautiously beside Samuel, stretching her head far out of her shell, straining to look in every direction. They followed closely behind Frieda and Bu Zard while Wanda ran ahead to catch her children.

As Samuel's large tail swished past the gate, a buzzer sounded and the electronic gates slammed shut with a bang. The animals all jumped from the loud noise.

"Well, that decided that," said Bu Zard, secretly glad that the alligator was inside the park with him. "We're all inside now." The vulture had not wanted to be alone in the park with Frieda, who jumped at the sight of her shadow.

"*Tch, tch, tch,*" Frieda croaked. Her worst fears had just come true. The gates closed behind them, locking them in.

The small group caught up to Tony and Sophie. Wanda was furious with them.

"But, Mom, look! It's beautiful," Tony said.

The animals turned to see what Tony was talking about. White sand beaches lay beyond the river. The white sand was dotted with palms and multi-colored exotic plants that provided refuge from the sun. Picnic tables were scattered throughout the area and covered in red and white checkered tablecloths. Picnic baskets sat on each table, some open with food spilling out, others closed and sitting undisturbed.

On the right side of the beach, a small park was being invaded by families of water fowl. The babies played in the fountains and slid down mini water slides, while the adults perched atop every tree, pole, or sprinkler head in sight.

To the left, a giant replica of a mountain volcano sent bubbling water out of the top, spilling it down the sides. A stream flowed all the way down its backside, shooting out into the river and onto the hordes of rafters and swimmers floating by. On the front side of the mountain, a sheer cliff jutted out, forming the top of a waterfall that powered a small Ferris wheel with multi-colored buckets to carry the riders. As the water flowed over the cliff and poured into the buckets, the Ferris wheel turned in a circle, allowing each of the riders to be soaked as they reached the top and then rode down.

"I want to do that," said Sophie as she looked from side to side, trying to see everything.

Tony answered, "Me too, I want to do that and that and that and—"

"Don't forget why we're here," said Desta, cutting Tony off. "We've got to get to the animals and warn them about the trucks."

Bu Zard spotted Benson and Della flying above the trees and sent Frieda to bring them down.

Benson and Della had continued with their mission to coordinate a time for the animals to meet with Bu Zard and Samuel.

"I'm not hearing much enthusiasm for a meeting," Benson said. "The best plan I could work out is that some of the animals will meet with us tonight *after* the rides shut down. They're all staying in the Hamlet at the Maki Maki Resort. It's a little village in the center of the resort."

"How long till the rides shut down?" asked Frieda.

"Sunset," said Della. "We have four hours."

"But we may not have till sunset," said Bu Zard while pacing. "We have no idea when they're going to start moving the animals with those trucks. Or if that's even what they plan on doing."

"Let's split up and try to talk to as many animals as we can," said Samuel. "And *don't*, I mean, *absolutely do not trust anyone*."

Desta, Tony, and Sophie started for the wooden bridge, without looking back at the adults.

"Children," Wanda called, ready to stop them before they disappeared into the park.

Three pairs of eyes turned to look at Wanda.

"This is too dangerous. We've got to stick together." But the crestfallen faces of her children made Wanda rethink the situation. She looked around the water park. Animals were having a great time everywhere. It couldn't hurt to let the kids play on a few of the rides. Pushing aside the memory of the trucks waiting beside the gates, she relented. "Well maybe a few rides while I talk to the animals."

Tony and Sophie looked at each other then ran, kicking their heels in delight, to the top of the bridge. There they stopped and waited for Desta to catch up.

A dangerous run

Victor jumped from yard to yard, with the dogs and wildlife officers hot on his tail as he led them away from Maurice and Jason. It became immediately clear that reaching Gulf Hammock safely was going to be hard. He jumped a fence and landed on a row of trashcans stacked on the other side. As he struggled to his feet, he became entangled in the lids and garbage that had rolled out onto the ground. The dogs ran around the fence and almost caught him as he came out of the yard and into the alley between the houses.

Victor looked around. He was caught between the dogs chasing him and a very busy road. He made a quick decision. He ran through oncoming traffic to get to the other side of the road, hoping this would keep the dogs from following him. But the steady line of cars coming from both directions caused him to stop on the center line of the road. Cars, horns blowing, whizzed by on both sides, so close that he could feel a breeze as they passed him. The dogs ran along the road shoulders, baying and barking at the buck trying to elude them.

At some point in the chase, the wildlife control officers realized their dogs were after a deer and not a bear. The officers began using their dog whistles to retrieve their hounds.

"I'll get you next time," yelled a large bloodhound running down the side of the road. The dog turned and sniffed the ground, hoping to pick up the scent of the bear.

Victor made it to the opposite side of the road and caught sight of the dogs as they reacquired Jason's scent. They immediately ran wildly in the opposite direction, ears flopping against their heads. Victor could only hope he had given Maurice and Jason enough time to get away.

But the big buck had little time to worry about the other two. A group of boys playing in a ball field spotted the deer and started their own chase, throwing baseballs and rocks at him that he dodged by weaving in and out of trees.

Victor finally reached the outskirts of the Hammock, a pine forest, northwest of Ocala. He was tired and worn-out from the run he had just made. He hoped it was the most dangerous thing he would have to do on this trip.

The Hammock spread out for acres in front of him and he decided his best bet would be to move deep into the forest before resting. After an hour of walking through rows of planted pines, the ground covered in soft pine needles, he came to a stand of hardwoods overgrown with bushes and vines. The spot offered him a place to rest and figure out his next move.

He had to find the rendezvous spot where he would meet Maurice and Jason. He didn't know where Cypress Point was. He had never been there and Maurice had no time to give directions before they separated. Victor also needed another plan in case Maurice and Jason didn't make it out of Ocala. The bear could not move as swiftly as Maurice, and the dogs had been hot on their tail once they stopped following him. The only chance they had to arrive safely would be with Maurice. Thankfully, the bobcat was smart.

Victor looked into the trees for any birds. They would carry the first news of the bear and the bobcat. From tree to tree, they'd report the arrival of strangers to the Hammock. The animals in the Hammock weren't part of the truce in the Everglades, so they'd be leery of strangers.

Two hours later, the first agitated bird calls began. The crows started the story. Then it was picked up by the mockingbirds and doves. A blue-jay landed in the tree above Victor. He called out to his family. "A bobcat is in the woods, bobcat in the woods! Be careful, be careful!"

Well, thought Victor, *Maurice made it*. Now he needed to follow the birds to locate the bobcat and find out if Jason was as lucky.

Chapter 24
They Won't Listen

Desta walked behind Tony and Sophie. They headed deep into the park in search of water rides. The little turtle wasn't happy about being inside the park, especially after the gates were locked the minute they had stepped inside.

"Don't you think this is a little creepy?" she said to Tony. The park lay in every direction, and as far as Desta could see, there were no employees *anywhere*. No humans, just animals from the Animal March.

"What?" asked Tony.

"All those trucks waiting right outside the gate. Don't you think that's creepy?"

"Don't worry so much, Desta. Mom and Samuel are right behind us," Tony said before the turtle could explain all her reasons for her uneasiness. "Who's going to mess with us and a fifteen-foot alligator?"

Desta looked back at Wanda and Samuel. The adults were aggressively cornering a family of armadillos that obviously was not interested in what the two larger animals were telling them about their "free vacation." The armadillos kept trying to get away. They wiggled and spun, edging themselves closer and closer to a small waterway. Just when Wanda seemed to have them cornered, they jumped one-by-one onto a rubber raft and floated away.

"Well," said Wanda with a huff. "They certainly were *not* ready to listen. Maybe we'll have some luck with the parents waiting for their children at the bottom of the rides. They'll have nothing to do while they wait and it won't be so easy for them to get away."

"And we can try the rides?" asked Tony.

"Sure. Let's go," said Wanda.

Desta followed Tony and Sophie, grudgingly, to the first ride where she temporarily forgot all about her fears. The three young ones got themselves drenched while riding the colorful Ferris wheel, going round and round under the waterfall. Then they climbed to the top of the famous hurricane water slide. The spiral ride was loaded with tight turns and drop-off curves that sent the three friends speeding into a man-made pond at the bottom.

But Desta's gut was telling her they were in danger. She just could not figure out what the danger was. Everywhere she looked, the animals were having a grand time. They played and frolicked in the water. On the surface, everything seemed so safe and secure, so why was she having these bad feelings?

She kept mentioning her uneasiness to Tony, but the deer brushed away her fears, while motioning toward Samuel.

"We're fine," Tony kept saying.

Wanda and Samuel stayed close by, which should have helped to reassure Desta. At the moment, the two adults had a mother and father otters' undivided attention. Wanda had them blocked by standing in front of them. Samuel had them trapped by lying directly behind them. Wanda talked away, the whole time acting oblivious to the otters' disapproving glances.

Tony and Desta made their way over to what proved to be an awkward situation.

"There are large trucks waiting right outside the back gate," Wanda told the otters.

"Waiting for what?" asked the father otter. "And what does that have to do with us?"

"We're not sure," said Samuel. "We think they have a relocation plan and the trucks are part of it."

"Well, I'm not getting into a truck," said the mother otter. "Are you getting into a truck, Darryl?"

The father otter shook his head no.

"Okay, then. There you have it. We're fine and we can enjoy the park. Thanks for telling us. Toodaloo," said the mother otter.

Wanda and Samuel had no choice but to let the otter couple go so they could join their children.

Desta shook her head at the spectacle that she had just witnessed. It was true. T.J. and the man couldn't make the animals get into the trucks. Could they? No, this many animals could never be forced into the trucks. So, why not have fun? She crawled away to join her friends on a raft ride down the Booma Booma White Water River, putting the trucks outside the back gates firmly out of her mind. They finished their raft ride just in time to watch Samuel and Wanda approach a cement pond full of frogs, toads, and salamanders having a pool party. The party quickly broke up when Samuel walked into the middle of the pond, swinging his large tail back and forth. The party participants hopped and crawled in all directions.

Desta had to laugh, which helped to lighten the mood that she had been in for most of the day.

"Samuel, it's going to be hard to talk to the animals if you keep scaring them away," Wanda said to the alligator just as Desta approached.

Wanda turned to the children. "Hey, it's getting late. Are you ready to head to the village? We're seeing fewer and fewer animals out here. Maybe they're calling it a day already."

That's it, thought Desta. That's what was nagging her. There weren't any people and the park had become a lot less crowded with the animals. The lines had been long when they first arrived, wrapping up and down the aisles designated as waiting. But now, there were hardly any animals waiting in the lines.

"Maybe they're floating on the Bayou River," said Tony.

The Bayou River was a slow-moving river that filled a man-made concrete riverbed and completely encircled the park.

"We'll check there and follow it around to the village entrance. That's where we're supposed to meet Bu Zard," said Wanda.

On the way to the river, Desta noticed something else that added to her suspicions. In all the picnic areas, the animals were taking naps. Everywhere! It wasn't that they were sleeping that caught her attention. It was that they looked like they'd fallen asleep in the middle of eating. They lay on the tables by the opened picnic baskets, on the ground, and on the benches—most of them with their mouths open and all of them snoring.

"Tony, check out the animals in the picnic areas. They're all sleeping."

"Yeah, this water park fun is tiring. I could go for a snooze myself," Tony said.

"But, something's not right. They all seem . . . they seem unconscious." Desta watched a raccoon sift through the picnic leftovers of a bear family that lay sleeping nearby. He took a big bite and then immediately curled up and went to sleep beside one of the bears. Desta shook her head. "Bizarre. It's just all bizarre."

"Stop worrying, Desta. They're just tired from the water park. Look! There's a group of animals waiting by the river."

Desta followed Tony's gaze to the river that lay ahead. A group of animals formed several lines and they were waiting their turn to grab a raft or small boat. The little turtle forgot all about the sleeping animals as soon as she got to the Bayou River.

The river was full of animals from the walk. Some drifted by on plastic inner tubes, while others swam. Wanda let the three young friends climb aboard a raft and float the rest of the way to the village.

Vacations don't just fall from the sky

Bu Zard spent his afternoon preparing a speech and trying it out on any animal that would listen. Frieda tagged along, critiquing his performance and giving him feedback on his sincerity as well as his persuasiveness.

"My fellow animals," he began, speaking to a small group of beavers that paused for a moment to listen to Bu Zard. "I'm sure it's clear to you that this vacation is simply a distraction. There are forces working against us. This should be obvious to you by now. Vacations don't really fall from the sky."

The beavers shook their heads in disagreement and hurried away.

"That's ridiculous, Bu Zard," Frieda said while eating small fish from a picnic basket. "This vacation totally came from the sky. In fact, it came from an airplane that was flying in the sky and, quite honestly, whoever is behind this knows exactly what they're doing. Look at all the food we've been given, and the accommodations are wonderful. Someone has thought of everything."

"My fellow animals," he said, using a different approach on a large, black bear that growled at Bu Zard and immediately walked away.

Bu Zard yelled after the bear, "While we stay here . . . " He raised his voice as his intended audience got further away. "Having the time of our lives . . . " He got louder. "The Everglades are slowly being destroyed. Our families and friends, who are depending on us, are at this very moment losing their homes."

"Wonderful, Bu Zard," Frieda said, and then, swallowing a big mouthful of herring, she continued. "If all else fails, use guilt to get them back on the walk."

This prompted Bu Zard to try his favorite line. "Trust me, friends. Right now, a caravan of trucks awaits you outside the gate to take you to who-knows-where, probably someplace where you will *never* see your friends or family again."

"No, Bu Zard," Frieda said. "You cannot say, 'Trust me.' The animals won't listen. Especially when they find out how you deceived them. You really need some sort of proof that they're in danger. These animals are having a blast right now. They'll never *trust you*."

Bu Zard knew Frieda was right about the animals. This place was amazing and fun. "I hope the rest of our group is having some luck. I need a little support when we start explaining those trucks to the animals."

"Well, all we can do now is wait and see who's going to show up," said Frieda. But as she looked out into the park, it was obvious to her that all the animals were having a great time. She was having doubts that they would even want to listen.

"We'll never get them to Tallahassee to meet with our legislative representatives," said Bu Zard, who was having his own doubts.

"Right now, you had better hope that we can get them all out of this park safely," Frieda said. She did not get a chance to elaborate further. A bell rang over all the loud speakers in the park, causing both birds to stop talking.

It was 6:15 p.m. and the bell signaled that the water park was shutting down for the night. When the bell stopped, Bu Zard shrugged his wings and said, "Come on, Frieda, I think we're about to find out what this vacation is all about. . . . Good or bad."

Chapter 25
Let's Ask a Panther

On the west side of the state, deep inside Gulf Hammock, Maurice sat on a limb, watching Victor make his way cautiously to an old scrub oak that stood on the edge of a cypress swamp. The cat's short stubby tail moved back and forth.

"Well, well, looks like you made it," said Maurice.

"Yeah, so did you. But where is Jason?" asked Victor.

In answer to his question, a limb above his head snapped and the big bear tumbled into the shallow, stale water of the swamp, just missing a cypress knee sticking out of the water.

"I told you that limb was too small for you to climb out on," said Maurice.

Jason looked over at the buck and slowly got to his feet. "I made it, no sweat," said Jason.

"Right, no sweat," Maurice said sarcastically. "All I can say is that this is one slow dude. We had to double back over our trail five or six times to confuse the dogs. We ran down drainage ditches and through holding ponds to cover our scent. You know, it's hard to find standing water in the middle of a city."

Maurice paused and pointed toward the road. "Anyway, I think we lost them. But, just to be safe and because I didn't want to take any chances with our boy here, I brought him to this swamp to complete the confusion."

Maurice followed a limb back over to dry land and jumped down near Victor.

"What next? Where do you want to go from here?" asked the bobcat.

Victor shook his head. "I've tried to get some information from the birds about the Animal March. None of them will talk. I haven't even heard a mention in passing about the march. It's like it never existed. Something as big and important as the Animal March should be a major topic of conversation—even here in the Hammock. This is a first, a historic event. Never have this many animals united for a single cause. I'm puzzled and I'm worried."

"Maybe we should just sit here in the woods," said Jason. "With my prior history, I don't think it's such a good idea for me to show up in Tallahassee."

"*Now* you're concerned about going into a city? Didn't seem to bother you earlier today," said Maurice.

"Look, you two. I'm worried about my family," said Victor. "Something's not right. Why aren't the animals talking about the march? I'm feeling very uneasy about leaving Wanda and the kids."

"If it will make you feel any better," said Maurice. "I know a panther that lives in these woods. She moved away from the 'Glades years ago after most of her family had died or disappeared. It was hard on her. After her brother was run over by a car on Alligator Alley, she left the 'Glades for good and wound up here."

“Oh, that’s a great idea,” said Jason. “Go out and *look* for a panther.”

“You think she’ll know what’s up?” asked Victor, ignoring the bear’s comment.

“She’ll know,” answered Maurice. “She stayed in contact with her friends down in the Everglades. She’s a resourceful cat.”

“Yeah, but a panther, they typically don’t want to be found,” said Jason. “How are you going to find her?”

“*We* don’t find her,” answered Maurice. “*She* finds us.”

Chapter 26

The Opossum is Not Our Friend

Bu Zard stood on a stage he had found in the center of the village square. "This is perfect for my speech tonight," he told Frieda. "You can see all the streets from up here. It's the best place to get a lot of attention."

It was obvious that the animals were reluctant to attend the speech. Very few had arrived (although the park had been closed for at least an hour), and none of them would make eye contact with Bu Zard.

Frieda sat at the back of the stage and was no longer paying attention to the vulture. Instead, she hummed and whistled as if she had no cares in the world.

Bu Zard shrugged his shoulders and threw up his wings. He was aggravated with Frieda. She was not taking this seriously. This was a reversal. *She* usually griped *at him* to be more serious. This park was getting to all of them. He turned his back on his friend so he could concentrate and began rehearsing his speech one more time.

Wanda and Samuel's small group took up positions to the side of the stage, keeping the children close by. Benson and Della were there, along with a few other birds, but the crowd was small and definitely not ready to continue the march.

"Bu Zard, the animals have lost their focus," said Frieda, as she lay flat on the floor of the stage. "Their hearts must not have been in it to start with if they could be sidetracked like this."

Bu Zard agreed with Frieda. He definitely could not use the 'Trust me' speech right now.

A bell in the distance clanged. The sound filled the air and grew louder. Bu Zard glanced nervously in the direction of the clanging noise. He looked for his friends gathered close to the stage.

"Come on, Frieda," he said. "We need to get to Samuel and the rest of our group. We may need to make a run for it."

"Oh, silly you," said Frieda. "We're birds. We don't run! We march, *ha, ha, ha*."

Bu Zard looked at his friend who was now holding her wings in front of her face while checking out the tips of each feather as if they were the most interesting things on earth.

"Come on, Frieda. Get up now!"

A few animals appeared on balconies, while others came into the square where Bu Zard had arranged to give his speech.

A red fire engine, driven by the man with the blue necktie and yellow half-moons, came slowly up the street. MAKI MAKI RESORT FIRE DEPARTMENT was written on the side. T.J., the opossum, sat on the top, wearing a black fire helmet.

The man drove the firetruck into the town square and brought it to a stop in front of the stage, blocking Bu Zard and Frieda from the group. He continued to ring the siren and bell for several minutes until a large crowd gathered.

T.J., the opossum, sat on the top of the firetruck, wearing a black fire helmet.

"Welcome, my friends," called T.J. to the crowd. "Have you had a wonderful day?"

A cheer went up from the animals, followed by hooting, whistles, and claps.

Bu Zard tried to get Frieda to move across the stage. This was not easy because she wasn't helping at all. Bu Zard looked around in panic. He couldn't leave her up here. The blue heron giggled every time he touched her. This was more than a loss of focus. Frieda had lost her ability to think rationally. She was acting completely wacky and Bu Zard wondered if this had something to do with the opossum's scheme. Bu Zard used both his wings and pushed and pulled Frieda as fast as he could to the edge of the stage.

Homes of the future

Desta tapped Tony on the foot. "Whatever the opossum has to say, I don't trust him and this is not going to be good for the march."

The large, red fire engine blocked the floor of the stage where Bu Zard was frantically trying to move Frieda to the edge.

"My friends." The opossum waited a moment for the cheering to stop. He moved to the center of the truck's roof and opened a large, black case. "My friends, we are so glad you could join us at the beautiful Maki Maki Resort. We hope you are having a good time."

The crowd of animals continued to grow and T.J. paused again to allow the cheering to stop and the rest of the animals to get into the town square. On every corner, pink pigs were opening food booths and giving out free samples. The smell of delicious foods filled the air. The animals wasted no time getting to the square for the opossum and the treats that were waiting for them.

"My employers have arranged this wonderful vacation for you and there is much more to come," said the opossum, while flashing a toothy smile at the audience.

T.J. reached down and turned on a computer connected to a projector inside the black case. It was aimed above the stage and high enough for the animals to see from wherever they stood. Pictures flashed at the top of the block wall supporting the stage. A PowerPoint presentation began.

Desta strained to see the images as they appeared, catching glimpses from where she waited with her friends. She knew it was something big because the crowd became very quiet.

"As you can see, the Everglades, where we have all lived for many years, is in serious deterioration." The opossum pushed a button and pictures flashed on the screen. "Weeds are clogging the water system and, for some unknown reason, the water is making the animals sick, including many of you."

Desta watched Bu Zard, who was struggling at the edge of the stage with Frieda and waving one wing wildly at Wanda. Wanda was so absorbed in what was going on above the stage floor that she didn't notice. Bu Zard struggled a moment more with his friend, then raised his wings as if he didn't know what to do. After looking around he gave Frieda a shove with his wing, sending the blue heron tumbling to the ground. After flying down to check on her, he walked over to Desta.

"Keep your eyes on Frieda," he said to Desta. "I don't know what's wrong with her. I've got to see what the opossum is doing."

Desta watched Bu Zard as he flew to a position on a nearby roof where he had a better view of the presentation.

A new picture flashed overhead, showing a dried-up water area, followed by a picture of a forest fire.

T.J. continued, "And if the droughts aren't bad enough, we have fires that put all of our lives in danger and burn up thousands of acres every year. I want you all to know that my employer has been working hard to come up with a solution to our problem."

The animals nodded in agreement. Some even wept at the sight of the Everglades' condition in the pictures. Food hawkers hurried around giving out samples and patting the animals on the backs.

T.J. put his paw in front of the light, casting a shadow on the screen. Taking one claw, he pointed at the next picture and a sign in front of a large office building. "HM Consolidated Enterprises has a plan for all of the animals that will ensure your safety and put your minds at ease. We can make your life a lot more comfortable than what it has been in the past. Why should we live in such a dangerous place as the Everglades? Let's let the people build their homes there. Half-Moon Enterprises is prepared to do that, while providing a much better home and environment for all of you and your families."

The animals leaned forward in anticipation of what the opossum was about to say.

Desta tapped Tony hard on his hoof. "This isn't good. HM is the bad guy in the Everglades. They're polluting the water. And—and what's wrong with Frieda?"

Tony looked in the direction that Desta was looking and saw Frieda lying in a heap below the stage.

"Let me tell Mom," said Tony.

"We all know that HM has been the main polluter," Desta heard Samuel say. "And now they're saying they want to build houses on areas of their land that run deep into the Everglades. I thought Bu Zard said he made that up. I think he may have exposed their plan by accident."

The opossum went on. "We have been building communities—we call them *homes of the future*." This was said with an emphasis on the *future*. "We want to take the everyday risk out of living. We want to ensure the animals have a safe place to raise their families, have plenty to eat, and have clean, fresh water to drink."

The pictures above the stage clicked faster. The pictures were of animals living in cozy habitats. Food was conveniently located next to each animal's shelter. All of the animals appeared to be relaxed and tranquil.

"Over the next few days, we want to show you our *homes of the future*. We have graciously arranged transportation to visit Half-Moon Acres' *Homes and Land* in beautiful North Florida." The opossum paused to allow for the cheering and clapping animals to quiet down.

Desta lost sight of Bu Zard as he flew to the top of the fire engine while blowing his bright red whistle, trying to get the attention of the animals. Then she heard the vulture shout,

"Wait, wait! It's a trick! They want to stop our mission to save the Everglades. We can't just give up on our march. We can't let our families down. We are meeting with our representatives, and we . . . " The animals were dancing and singing. It was impossible for Desta to hear Bu Zard's speech above the noise. Music played over the loud speakers and more pictures of 'the future' flashed on the overhead screen.

Bu Zard could not finish because the opossum interrupted him. "The legislature will help fund this new residence for all animals," T.J. told the animals. "We will bring your families to join you. This is a wonderful opportunity and you need to see it *before* you make any decisions." He paused, and then added dramatically, "This is the future. This is our future! We will let the state take care of us!"

The fire engine's siren blared, adding to the noise and confusion. Then the man drove the fire engine away from the stage, narrowly missing animals as he went.

Bu Zard flew back to the stage to talk some sense into the partying animals.

After several more minutes of trying to speak to the animals, Bu Zard gave up and flew down to be with his friends. "Can you believe that?" he said. "Their plans are crazy. They want to relocate the animals. All the animals!"

"I think you hit a nerve, Bu Zard," said Samuel. "Your rumor of development in the Everglades was very close to the truth."

"What do we do now?" said the vulture. "The animals are in a frenzy. They're not going to listen to anything we have to tell them now."

"Let's get out of here," Samuel told the group. "Let's get out, quick! Something bad is happening. I just can't figure out what."

They all turned to look at Frieda who lay motionless on the ground.

"We've got to get Frieda. I'm not leaving without her," Bu Zard yelled to them.

A few feet from Frieda, Jason's mother, Elda, had collapsed on the ground. Her cubs curled up beside her. Bu Zard hurried over and shook each of them with his wings, trying to get a response—any response. But, nothing happened. Elda was as much out of it as Frieda, both of them in a heavy sleep. It appeared as if all the animals were falling to the ground and going straight to sleep.

"What's wrong with them?" asked the big gator.

"I don't know. I just don't have a clue," answered Bu Zard. He looked around helplessly at the scene. "Let's get to the outside of the park. We'll worry about it there."

Desta stayed close to her friends. In no way did she want to be left behind.

Chapter 27

Who's Really in the Trap?

"Okay, Victor," Maurice called to the deer. "Stay right there. No, move a little to the right. Yeah, right there. I can see you clearly now. No limbs or trees are blocking the view." Maurice and Victor worked busily on their plan to capture Sara, the panther.

Maurice gave a few more instructions to the deer on where to stand while they tried to lure Sara in close. He knew this was probably not his smartest plan; panthers tended to get a little mean when they were cornered. But, he had no other way of asking her if she had any news about the Animal March, and it was definitely important to find out where the animals were *before* they went into Tallahassee with Jason.

"Maurice, I'm not too happy with being the bait here," the deer pointed out.

"Well, I would have used Jason if I could, but Sara isn't going to go for it," the bobcat said. "Don't worry. I've got the trap ready for her. She'll never get to you."

Maurice backed away from the hole he had covered with branches and leaves. Very carefully, he backed along the path he had walked in on, using a trick that cats in *his* family had used for years.

“We don’t want to make her too mad,” Maurice said. “She may not want to tell us anything.”

With that comment, Maurice looked up and noticed Victor’s eyes had grown very round. Bam! He bumped into an immovable object and, from the feel of fur on fur, he could tell it was not a tree. “Let me guess,” he whispered barely breathing. “She’s behind me.”

Victor nodded slowly.

Maurice started to run but the panther slammed a paw down on his neck, stopping him in his tracks and knocking him to the ground. The panther was twice the size of Maurice and she towered over him as she spoke.

“Where do you think you’re going?” she asked. “And what is it I won’t go for? Huh? Your little trap you spent all evening building? It’s been very amusing watching you work so hard, Maurice. If you were a smart cat, you would have made that lazy bear do the digging.”

Sara looked over at a nearby pine tree where Jason lay sleeping. “You really have lowered your standards, Victor,” she said, using the deer’s name and surprising both the deer and the bobcat.

“Have we met?” Victor asked, somewhat confused.

“Of course not. I know you.” She slapped a big paw against the side of Maurice’s head. “I’ve been watching you since you came to the Hammock. I could have had you several times—you and these other two losers. You are forgetting to be careful on this trip. Not all animals are part of the truce in the ’Glades.”

“You know then?” Victor spoke. “You know about the plan?”

"I know about the Animal March," she answered. "I just can't figure out why you and this foolish cat are *here*, in the Hammock."

"I owed a favor to Jason's father," answered the buck.

The bobcat, that had been too terrified to talk or move until now, looked up at Victor.

Victor continued, hoping to gain the panther's trust, "When I was young, a hunter had a clear shot that would probably have hit and killed me—Jason's father warned me. He growled and the hunter turned and shot him." Victor paused, his voice catching in his throat, but after a moment was able to continue with the story. "I never spoke of it or told anyone but it has always stayed with me. When I saw Jason's mother pleading with Samuel and Bu Zard, I knew I had to do something. I had to repay Jason's father."

Jason made a sound by the tree, bringing the attention of the three animals to him. "So that's what happened to my dad," he said. "The birds told Mom he had been shot. I was just a young cub and never got to know him."

Sara yawned. "Okay, okay, never mind. Sorry I asked. The question *is* how do I deal with you three? You were planning on trapping me. Did you really think you could get away with that plan? I'm a little hurt that you thought me so stupid."

"Sara," said the deer, "I know we have never met and I know nothing about you or why you left the Everglades. I don't even know if you care about the animals, the water, or the future of the Everglades. But it is all slowly being destroyed, and we felt strongly enough to risk everything and seek out help."

Sara looked at the buck for a moment. Then she smacked the bobcat, sending him flying toward the deer. "What do you think I can do for you? I left there a long time ago. It just brings back sad memories of family and friends I've lost. I came here to get away from those memories but this place is slowly becoming overcrowded. I don't know where I'll go next."

"Come with us," said Victor. "Come with us to Tallahassee. You can be there when we ask for help from the Governor. This affects us all, Sara, even you and the animals in the Hammock."

Sara looked from animal to animal, weighing her options before speaking.

"I don't know," she said. "Did you know the animals from the march are at a water park in Orlando? How can you be sure that there will be a march after today? It seems to me that it is, more than likely, finished."

Victor's and Maurice's jaws dropped as they turned and looked at each other in stunned silence.

"In fact, to continue to Tallahassee could be quite dangerous. Especially if it's just you two with a marked bear," Sara said, reminding them of Jason's two prior captures.

Jason overheard everything and walked over to join Maurice and Victor.

"Now what do we do?" the bear asked.

Chapter 28
Don’t Eat the Herring

Benson and Della helped Bu Zard’s small group find a way out of the water park.

“I saw an opening by the food service entrance,” said Benson. “We can get you out through there.”

The going was tough with Frieda. Bu Zard and Wanda pulled the blue heron across the park. Bu Zard had to use his beak to hold one of the bird’s long legs. Wanda used her mouth to pull the other leg. Frieda’s wings dragged behind her head, which bumped along the ground.

“Wow, this is not how I thought the Animal March would end,” said Desta. “This has turned into a big mess. I miss my mother and all my new brothers and sisters.”

“I miss the Everglades,” said Tony. “I want to go home.”

“We are,” Wanda responded. “Just as soon as we get out of here, we are going home.”

Benson flew down and pointed to a building in front of the group. “The service entrance is on the back side,” he told them. “The gate is unlocked and opened and a food delivery van is parked there.”

“Food. Yeah, food is something I have not thought about much today,” said Bu Zard, after dropping Frieda’s leg to take

“Wow, this is not how I thought the Animal March would end.”

a short rest. "Did you see the meals they had in there? Anything you could wish for was available to eat."

"No, I didn't eat," said Wanda. "Samuel and I were out talking to the animals all afternoon. We just never had time."

"We were having such a good time on the rides that we didn't take time to eat," said Desta, looking up at her friends.

Benson told them that neither he nor Della had ever made it to the picnic baskets that were scattered about the park.

"Well, I didn't eat," Bu Zard told them all. "I worked on my speech. Frieda must have been the only one who filled her belly. She gulped down herring all afternoon."

"That's it," said Desta and Tony at the same time.

"There had to be something in the food," Desta explained. "It's the only thing Frieda did that we didn't do—eat. The other animals were there all day and would have eaten some of the goodies too. That must be why they are sleeping in all the picnic areas."

"I know Elda ate," said Wanda. "I saw her take food from the vendors during the opossum's speech, and then she lay down with her cubs. We've got to go back and get her."

"No!" said Benson and Della together.

"This is the only unlocked exit out of here," said Della. "We've checked all the others."

"It would be risky to go back. You could get locked in," said Benson. "Let's get to the outside and then talk about what we can do."

"We're not going back, that's for sure," said Samuel. "We'll worry about the others as soon as *we* are safe. Right now, let's get as far away from here as we can."

Desta looked around at the group. Her mouth quivered. "But my aunt is in there and twenty-two of my first cousins. We're just going to leave them?"

"We don't have a choice," Samuel said. "We can't help them if we fall asleep too. We'll think of something. Don't worry. I've got quite a few relatives in there myself."

Bu Zard was still struggling with Frieda. He shook her hard with his claw, but he could not get her to wake up. She lay on the ground with her beak open and snored.

"Throw her over Samuel's back," said Benson.

It took the entire group to get the unconscious bird over Samuel's back. Desta climbed on the alligator with Frieda to hold the bird steady.

With Benson leading the way, the group slipped out the park's back service gate, leaving their friends behind.

Desta rode in silence as they passed through the gate. Her worries from earlier in the day came rushing back. Now she knew the animals would not be forced into the trucks. That had never been the intention. The devious opossum had planned on putting the animals to sleep all along. There would be no opposition. She could not help but wonder if she would ever see the animals again.

No time for looking back

Miles to the northwest of Hurricane Hamlet Water Park, Victor, Maurice, and Jason continued their trip to Tallahassee. Now, instead of freshwater lakes and streams that they had seen in abundance throughout central Florida, the trio walked a path that skimmed along saltwater marshes and brackish coastal water. The Gulf of Mexico lay to the west as they walked through forests of cabbage palms, pines, and red cedar. They skirted marshes surrounded by one-hundred-year-old cypress trees and live oaks thick with moss.

"Do you think Sara is really going to meet us?" Jason asked.

"Meet us or eat us," Maurice answered.

Victor looked at the cat out of the corner of his eyes.

"Just joking," said the bobcat. "I don't know what Sara is going to do. She said she would try to find out more about the Animal March and meet us when we get closer to the Capitol. She's a loner. I'd be more worried if she was walking along with us. She gets her feelings hurt very easily, if you know what I mean."

Victor walked along silently for a moment more and then said, "I still have an uneasy feeling. Maybe we should double back and check on the other animals. We could join up with them and be part of the march."

"No!" said Maurice and Jason together.

"We can't go back across the state. We left all of central Florida slightly mad at us," Maurice reminded the deer. "No, we need to go to Tallahassee. Bu Zard said he's arranged for TV and media coverage. We will be better off meeting the animals there."

"Did you forget what the panther told us?" asked Victor. "They might not make it."

"Then let's hope the cameras are rolling when we get into town," said Jason, as he glanced back at the two red marks painted on his rear. “I don’t believe that three red marks are an option.”

Chapter 29

What Do We Do Now?

"Where do we go now?" asked Tony as they walked out of the gate and into the back lot of the water park.

"We're going home," Wanda told him. "This whole thing has gotten out of hand. We'll send a message to your dad and tell him where we are."

Bu Zard could only follow along in silence. The Animal March had totally fallen apart and his best friend lay unconscious on Samuel's back. If she woke up now, she would probably die from the shock of being that close to the alligator.

The turkey vulture just wanted to get home and put this all behind him. But what was he going to tell the families waiting in the Everglades for their loved ones? He was fairly certain that he wasn't going to be quite as popular as he'd once envisioned—especially now that all the animals were about to be *relocated.*

Desta interrupted his thoughts. "Help! She's slipping," the turtle called out.

Frieda had somehow turned sideways on the back of the big gator and her feet were now dragging behind on the ground.

Bu Zard ran forward to help Desta steady the blue heron. While leaning over his friend, he heard a noise that caused his heart to beat rapidly—the sound of engines starting. One after another, the semi-tractor trailers were cranked and the ground vibrated as the big trucks roared to life. Bu Zard froze in his tracks.

A look of panic crossed each animal's face in the small group.

Benson and Della flew down to join them immediately.

"Mom," Sophie called out, fear in her voice. "Mom, the trucks! The animals! What's going to happen to them?"

"I don't know, Sophie honey. They'll be moved, I guess, to the new relocation center."

"We can't leave them," said Desta. "We have to do something."

"What?" Tony asked. "There are only nine of us, and one is unconscious. What can we do?"

Samuel moved his tail back and forth, causing Frieda to slip again. "Bu Zard," he said. "We can't leave."

"I know," said Bu Zard, with heaviness to his voice. He wanted to leave; the sound of those trucks had made the whole situation even scarier and unreal. "Benson, Della, could you fly above the park and let us know what's happening inside? Be careful. We don't know what they're capable of."

Wanda didn't like that idea. "I really think we should get back to the Everglades," she told the group. "Look at poor Frieda. We don't need to wind up like that."

"I have a bad feeling about this too," said Bu Zard. "Let's find a place to hide and watch for a while, at least until morning."

"Frieda is a good reason for us *to* stay," said Samuel. "We need to let her wake up. It won't be easy carrying an unconscious bird down the road. Bu Zard is right. Let's just wait until morning and see what happens to the animals. By then, maybe Frieda will be awake."

Bu Zard walked over to the mother deer and looked up into her eyes. "We can't leave yet. We've got to find out where those animals are going. I promise to get you and your family safely back to the Everglades. Wanda, it could be *us* in there right now."

The animals have been neutralized

Inside the water park, the music still played, but none of the animals were enjoying it. They had fallen into a deep sleep and lay wherever they had fallen.

At the town center, Ollie and T.J. waited while the man wearing the blue tie with yellow half-moons made a call to his bosses.

"We have the situation under control," he said into the phone. "The animals will no longer be a problem. They have been neutralized. We are starting to move them to the relocation center."

The man paused while he listened to the caller on the other end of the line. Then he responded. "No, there's no need to worry about them showing up in Tallahassee. The Animal March is officially over."

The man pushed the end button on his cell phone, then walked over to join the boar and the opossum. "A silent alarm came in from the back gate earlier," he told the two animals. "A small group of animals left through the service entrance before we could get it locked. I want you two to find them and pick them up. They can't be allowed to return to the Everglades or show up in Tallahassee. There can't be any witnesses."

"Where are we taking them?" asked Ollie.

"Use your head. Bring them to the relocation area or dispose of them. Do I have to tell you everything?"

Ollie and T.J. looked at each other and nodded their understanding.

"Meet me at the front entrance," T.J. told the boar. "There are cameras in the main office that have a continuous feed of the back lots. We'll review the video to figure out which way they headed after they left through the service entrance."

A short time later, T.J. rewound the video from the closed-circuit cameras.

"There, stop!" Ollie shouted into T.J.'s ear, causing the opossum to fall forward and onto the controls.

When T.J. straightened up, the picture was gone. He ran it forward and backward but all traces of Bu Zard and his small group were erased.

"Great, you've lost everything, you klutz," said T.J., his lips pulled back in a snarl. "Now we have to sniff them out. Be more careful!"

Ollie slumped out of the office, preferring to wait outside for the nasty opossum.

“I want you two to find them and pick them up.”

Chapter 30

We Need to Get Close

The first thing the animals did after leaving the park was hide. If they were going to wait until morning, they needed to be out of sight. Getting caught would mean certain relocation with the rest of the animals.

The bald eagles thought the best location was across the street from the back service entrance. The holding tanks that they had hidden behind earlier were in the best spot to watch the trucks. A maintenance building behind the tanks seemed the perfect place to put Frieda.

The animals took turns watching the activity at the back gate. They hid beside the buildings and used the storage tanks as barriers between the trucks and park gate. It was a great set-up because they could stay out of sight and peek around the tanks to watch all the activity.

"We need to get closer," said Samuel.

"How close?" asked Bu Zard.

Samuel looked at him, then shook his head in annoyance. "At least one of us needs to get close enough to hear their plans. We can't get good information from here."

Bu Zard swallowed and started to volunteer, but the tiniest animal in the group beat him to it.

"I'll go," Desta said, volunteering for the job. "I'm the smallest. No one will notice me."

"No, Desta," said Wanda. "It's too dangerous. You're too young. No, let an adult go."

The turtle was determined and began to argue immediately. "No one can get as close to the gate as me," said Desta. "My aunt is still in there. And my cousins! I'll be careful. I have to do it."

"She's right," said Samuel. "She is the smallest and has the best chance to get all the way to the gate without being seen. Bu Zard and I will follow and watch from behind the closest tank. If they spot her, or make any move toward Desta, we'll go in and get her. We won't let them take her," he said, in an attempt to reassure Wanda.

Desta took off crawling toward the fence before any of the animals could stop her.

Bu Zard and Samuel were right behind, hiding behind the tanks and watching the turtle as she made her way toward the activity outside the park.

The dimly lit parking lot made it hard to see what was going on between the trucks, and it was impossible to see inside the water park with the high, solid fences surrounding it. So Benson and Della flew high in the sky to keep an eye on the activity inside the park.

At twelve a.m., things started to happen. The first semi-tractor trailer backed up to a very large service entrance with double gates. Two pigs got out of the cab and came around to the rear of their truck.

Bu Zard and Samuel could not see anything from their hiding spot, and Samuel motioned for Bu Zard to move forward.

Great, thought Bu Zard. *My knees are knocking together and Samuel wants me to move forward.* The vulture dropped to the ground and wiggled over to the fence line before standing back up.

The gate opened and the turkey vulture could make out a shape that was unmistakable. T.J. came from inside the water park and waved at the two truckers, telling them it was okay to back in.

One of the pigs climbed onto the back of the truck and flicked a switch that lowered a ramp. He disappeared into the truck for a moment and then returned, driving a forklift that held stackable pallets.

Overhead, the eagles circled, flying lower and lower until it looked like they would touch the top of the trees. Bu Zard hoped the eagles could see what was going on inside the park without T.J. seeing them. The parking lot might be dimly lit, but the park was very bright and the two birds were visible, flying so low.

Bu Zard's heart pounded in his ears. There was nothing he could do but watch. He turned his attention to Desta as she moved along the fence line, crawling to within a few feet of the gate. *Be careful, be careful*, he thought. She was getting very close.

Nobody will notice they're missing

Desta moved a few feet forward at a time. She stopped and pulled her head into her shell, hoping her heart would stop racing. She didn't want to be caught and relocated with the other animals. She panted, taking in air with short, ragged gasps. Several times, she froze and couldn't move at all, not forward or backward. But after she sat still and let her heart slow down to a normal beat, she was able to make her legs carry her closer to the group gathering at the front gate.

"We're picking up the animals and loading them into containers now."

Desta heard the conversation and didn't need to see the animal speaking. She could recognize the voice of the nasty opossum from the gumbo-limbo tree anywhere.

"As soon as each truck is loaded, I want you to head north to the relocation facility. We need to get them there and unloaded into their habitats before they wake up. They're not going to be happy with their new homes," T.J. said.

"No problem, boss," said one of the truck drivers waiting by the gate.

"I've got to get back inside. We've got a situation. Some animals made it out one of the service entrances and we need to round them up. We can't have any rumors spreading back to the Everglades."

"You don't think a whole group of animals disappearing out of a water park is going to go unnoticed by the media, do you?" said the truck driver.

"Nobody pays attention to animals. They disappear every day all over America. What's a few hundred more…?" T.J. answered.

Desta's entire body began to tremble.

I know where they're hiding

T.J. finished giving directions to the truck drivers, then turned to make his way back into the park. A shadow passed over his head and he gave a quick glance at the sky. He knew immediately that the birds were the bald eagles that traveled with the Animal March. The opossum had noticed the birds earlier and had hoped they would go away, but as they circled overhead, he knew they were watching the activity in the park. He would have to take care of them sooner than later.

T.J. looked around to see if the man with the tie was near. He gave a big sigh of relief when he didn't spot him. The man had a serious temper problem when things didn't go his way. T.J. headed to the front office to find Ollie.

Ollie had fallen asleep in the corner of the small room.

"Ollie!" screamed the opossum. "You lazy pig! Why aren't you looking for those animals that got away? We've started loading the rest of them onto the trucks. We can't have them interfering or messing this up. The boss isn't going to like this."

"Just waiting on you T.J.," the boar mumbled. "I found them. They're hiding behind the chemical tanks by the maintenance shed. I saw that big gator's tail sticking out. Didn't want to get too close to *that*. So I thought *we* could make a plan."

"*WE?* Do I have to do everything?" T.J. screamed at him. "Get-a-truck-and-go-pick-them-up. Offer them a ride to the Everglades or something. Use your head for anything besides a snout rack."

T.J. stormed out of the office, slamming the door as he went. The noise got the attention of the man in the blue tie with yellow half-moons. He was on his way to check on his two employees.

"I don't know what I'm going to do with Ollie," T.J. complained to the man. "He's useless."

"Don't worry. After he finishes this job, we're getting rid of him too. We don't need the liability," the man said without any emotion.

Ollie jerked away from the door. He had overheard everything and didn't like what they were saying. He would just have to show them what a good job he could do.

Chapter 31
Follow Those Trucks

Desta was terrified. It had taken hours for her to move after overhearing the conversation. She stood in the center of the animals, her legs still shaking, and her heart still pounding, while she recounted every word she had overheard.

When Desta finished her story, the animals stood for a long moment of silence. They looked from one to another, very aware that they were in grave danger.

Adding to Desta's troubling tale were the eagles. Benson and Della returned from their scouting trip, describing the situation inside the park.

"They loaded the animals onto pallets with small tractors, then picked up the pallets and loaded those onto the trucks," said Benson

Samuels's tail moved back and forth, slowly at first, then faster as the eagles described the entire scene.

"Every last animal was put on those trucks. Even the frogs and lizards were scooped up and put into large bins, then loaded onto the pallets," said Della.

"Trucks have been pulling out of here all night," said Samuel. "One after another."

Bu Zard appealed to his friends, with wings raised in a shrug. "Now what do we do? They're gone. All the animals are gone. I can't go back to the Everglades and tell the families that I lost hundreds of animals. We have to have a plan."

"Well, what do you propose we do?" asked Wanda. "Frieda is still sleeping and it doesn't seem like she's going to wake up anytime soon. Not to mention, I have the three young ones to think about."

"We'll follow them," the big alligator said. "Benson and Della fly now and follow the trucks to see which direction they're headed. We'll start walking and you can come back to give us information. We cannot let them disappear forever."

Benson and Della immediately took off flying in the direction the trucks had taken.

Samuel turned to the group. "We're not going to let our neighbors down."

"We should get help," said Wanda. "Why don't we go to the TV stations?"

"The last time we were on television, the animals were all stampeding to go to a water park," said Samuel. "I don't know how much credibility we have at this point. But, it's an idea."

Bu Zard breathed out a sigh. He turned to Wanda. "You don't have to go with us. You can take your children and the turtle and head back home. If you stay in the woods you should be all right. We'll handle this alone," he added dramatically.

"We'll be okay, Mom," Tony said. "You'd want someone to help us if we were on those trucks."

"We'll walk with you as far as the highway," Wanda told Samuel and Bu Zard while ignoring Tony. "Then we'll head back to the 'Glades. I'll send help when I get back there. What about Frieda?"

"Put her on my back," said Samuel. "Find something to tie her on with."

Twenty minutes later, they had Frieda secure on the back of the enormous alligator. Della returned and told the animals the direction the trucks were heading.

"They are on the interstate headed north. Benson is following them. I'll bring you a report as soon as they make another turn," she said before flying off to rejoin her mate.

Desta rode with Frieda on Samuel's back while the other animals followed behind. They moved—although slowly—toward the Florida Turnpike.

Follow them

Ollie watched the animals from afar for several hours. When he saw them leave their hiding place, he hurried to the front entrance of Hurricane Hamlet to pick up a small box truck owned by a local plant nursery, parked in front of the gate. He found the truck unlocked and full of plants ready for delivery the next day. The boar emptied the truck of most of its contents, except for some needed equipment: shovels, picks, cutters, and a few chainsaws. He left those tools in the crates where he found them.

He pulled the truck out onto a side road and followed the small band of animals that he had been ordered to capture.

Chapter 32
A Bobcat with a Mission

Maurice, Victor, and Jason stood at the edge of a forest, looking into an open pasture outside the city of Tallahassee. They were being careful to stay far away from any major roads or residential areas. Jason's red markings identified him as trouble and they didn't want a visit from the wildlife control officers before they had a chance to get him to the Governor.

"Looks like we're getting close to people again," said Victor, nodding toward the pasture in front of them. The open land, cleared of all trees, had a neat white fence running around it. Cattle stood at the top of a distant hill, grazing on green grass, and a white farmhouse with a matching barn could be seen off to the right.

"What do we do now?" asked Jason. "We need a plan to find my mom and the other animals."

"*We* do nothing," answered Maurice. "Sara is trying to get information on the Animal March. Hopefully, we can depend on her. We need to find out what's happening with the Governor and the meetings at the Capitol. I can move faster if I do this by myself."

"I agree. We don't need to take you into the city until we know where the animals are," Victor said to Jason.

"I can be discreet," said Jason. "How do you think I got into the middle of town?"

Maurice and Victor simultaneously said, "NO!"

Jason frowned and sat with a heavy clunk onto the ground.

"Jason, your past history of breaking and entering makes it impossible to travel with you in the open. You are a wanted bear," said Maurice. "It's safer here. You and Victor can figure out a way to cover up the red bulls-eyes on your behind while I'm gone. It'll be easier to sneak you into the city without every person we come into contact with calling nine-one-one."

"Go ahead, Maurice," Victor said. "Get going. We'll be here when you get back." Then Victor said to Jason, "Let's go, buddy. There's some muck in the swamp that will cover up those spots, then we'll be ready to go when Maurice gets back." They headed back into the forest to find a swamp as Maurice took off for the city of Tallahassee.

Maurice moved much faster without the burden of his two companions. Victor was big and hard to hide while Jason was just plain slow. But now, by himself, the cat could hide in shadows and disappear into the tree branches before a person or animal could take a second glance. The bobcat was just slightly larger than a big tomcat and he hoped he could pass for one if the occasion arose.

It took several hours to make it to Tallahassee. The landscape changed from planted pines to open farmland to planted pines again. Finally, the rolling hills were dotted with houses in neat neighborhoods with manicured lawns. Instead of the pines, oak trees of all varieties stood in clusters, filling all the yards and providing Maurice with ample hiding spots as he approached Tallahassee. The sun was rising when he got to the first major street at the edge of town. The morning rush of traffic was just getting heavy and causing congestion at the intersections. Maurice didn't want to cross the traffic or risk being seen so he found a nice full oak to climb and take a nap, giving the morning commuters a chance to get where they were going before he approached the Capitol.

It was almost noon when he arrived at the Capitol. He had found it easily. The center tower was the tallest building in town and Maurice could see it from any open area. Two large, round domes sat atop buildings on either side of the tower, and Maurice approached the domed building on the south side of the tower first. He immediately looked for an animal that might give him information about the legislative meetings being held inside. He walked close to the concrete walls of the building, moving quickly from shadow to shadow. But everywhere he looked were humans. Not one animal was in sight. The bobcat decided to circle all the buildings. He had taken only a few steps, when a pigeon flew over his head and around the building that stood in front of the high rise.

Of course, thought Maurice, *the pigeons*. They lived in every city and were both curious and gossipy.

He followed the flight of the bird that had just flown above him. Walking around the building, he found a sign that told him he was at the Historic Capitol of Florida. This building had a lot more ledges, nooks and crannies, than the tower, making it an ideal place for pigeons to live. Maurice looked under the red- and white-striped awnings covering each of the windows in the Historic Capitol building. He was sure if he could find a pigeon that would talk to him, he would get his much-needed information about the sessions going on inside with the legislature.

While he searched the grounds of the Capitol for his gossiping pigeon, a large crowd gathered on the front lawn near the giant live oaks. Being naturally curious, he made his way over to the group.

A little girl, perched atop her father's shoulders, clapped her hands in rhythm to the music that came from the center of the circle of people. A young couple stood swaying to tunes and craning their heads to get a better view of the source of the sounds.

Maurice slipped between legs and around briefcases to get closer to the center. As he neared the front, he saw the pigeons he was looking for. They also kept rhythm to the music, swaying and cooing to the constant tap, tap, tapping.

In the center of the crowd, wearing captain's hats and matching ascots, tap dancing and singing to music coming from an MP3 player on a sound station: The Croc Brothers!

Wearing captain's hats and matching ascots, the Croc Brothers tap-danced and sang in the center of the crowd.

Chapter 33

The Fastest Way to the Turnpike

Bu Zard led his group down the sidewalk toward the Florida Turnpike. His mission had changed again. Now, instead of convincing the animals to continue their trip and follow him to Tallahassee, they were following the animals to rescue them. This mission was not going to be easy. Having Frieda strapped to Samuel's back made their progress painfully slow. More than once, the vulture had to adjust the straps that kept the bird from falling off. They had taken his red bag apart, using the straps as ties, but he was still having a hard time keeping her skinny neck and legs from sliding to the side and bumping along on the ground.

Motorists slowed to watch the group and blew their horns, but no one had stopped or offered any assistance to the slow-moving animals.

To make matters worse, a light spring rain started to fall. Bu Zard watched over the blue heron in a fatherly manner, wiping away the cool water that hit Frieda's beak and face. The drops of water began to have an effect on the sleeping bird.

Frieda opened her eyes, yawned, and tried to move a little, but the constraints that held her to the back of the giant alligator kept her in place. She tried to focus by opening and closing her eyes. She dozed several more times, but awoke fully when the rain became harder.

Bu Zard knew she was awake when she let out a loud shriek. Then panic set in. And finally, a terrified croak. "FRWAWK! Squawk!"

Wanda joined Bu Zard in comforting Frieda.

"There, there Frieda," Wanda murmured. "We're here. Your friends are here. Everything is fine." But the blue heron was in a full state of distress, making it hard to undo the straps.

"Hold still, Frieda," Bu Zard said, exasperation coming through in his tone. "I can't get these straps off if you don't hold still."

While Wanda and Bu Zard gave Frieda a brief explanation of why she was tied to Samuel's back, Desta watched a medium-sized truck, painted with NEW LEAF NURSERY on both sides, driving slowly behind them. The colors on the truck were very bright and the turtle had noticed it on several different occasions throughout the morning.

The truck slowly passed the animals. It pulled over to the curb in front of them. A large boar jumped out of the driver's side of the truck and walked around to the back. He wore a hat that said NEW LEAF NURSERY on the bill.

"Howdy," called the boar. "You creatures look like you're having a tough time there. Do you need some help?"

"No, we're okay," Bu Zard said. "We didn't mean to bother you."

"No bother," said the boar. "Where are you heading? Any place close by? Can I give you a lift? I just dropped off my morning deliveries. Got an empty truck, so there's plenty of room."

"We're trying to get to the turnpike," Bu Zard said.

"That's about eight miles from here," said the boar. "Why don't you let me give you a ride?"

Bu Zard looked at Frieda who was in no shape to walk or to ride on Samuel's back any longer. The rain came harder. Puddles of water formed in the road. A passing car splashed through one, sending a sheet of droplets over the animals. It had been a long night of watching the activities at the water park; the animals were close to total exhaustion.

"What do you think?" Bu Zard asked the group. "We could use a break. We can get a ride to the turnpike and give Frieda some time to fully wake up."

While Bu Zard talked, the boar went to the back of the truck and lowered the loading ramp to the ground. The back of the truck was empty except for a few crates stacked against the window of the cab. And at that moment, the dry interior of the truck looked inviting to them all.

"Okay," said Wanda. "A ride would be nice right now. When we get to the turnpike, we'll split up."

Desta tapped Tony's foot. "We shouldn't do this. We don't know this boar."

Tony shook his head. "We'll be fine."

Desta crawled over to Bu Zard. "This truck—" She did not get a chance to finish. The animals walked up the ramp and into the back of the truck. Desta looked around helplessly. All of the animals were now in the truck, waiting on her. The boar smiled and motioned, hurrying her along. There was nothing she could

"We shouldn't do this. We don't know this boar."

do but follow her friends. Staying alone on the side of the road would be worse. Once she got into the truck, she turned and watched as the boar raised the ramp and closed the doors, shutting out the light completely.

They heard a heavy clanking sound as the boar dropped the bolt in place across the back of the doors.

The inside of the truck was tight once all the animals packed into it. Samuel was a very large reptile and with three deer, two birds, and a turtle, there was not a lot of room. They would have been in total darkness except for small bits of light that shined under the door and at the very top of the window above the stacked crates. But when they had heard the clank of the bolt as it fell into place on the outside of the door, every one of them felt apprehension and uneasiness in the decision to accept the ride.

T.J.

The boar climbed into the driver's seat and started the engine. As he pulled away from the curb, he looked at the floorboard on the passenger side of the truck.

"Are you happy now?" the boar asked. "I told you I had it under control."

T.J. smiled and climbed up on the seat.

Chapter 34

Does Anybody Know What's Going On?

Maurice watched the Croc Brothers perform their dances for the audience gathered in front of the Historic Capitol building. At the end of each routine, the reptiles, using the ends of their canes, flipped their hats off while taking a deep bow. As the applause and yells for more filled the air, the brothers, in a show of synchronicity, dropped their hats onto the ground to catch the money that was tossed to them.

Larry turned off the MP3 player with a flick of his claw. This sent a signal to the crowd that the show was really over, and the onlookers began to disperse and go about their business.

Maurice waited for the brothers to finish before making his introduction. He watched the two younger Croc Brothers pick up the change on the ground that had missed their hats. The older brother shoved the music player into a canvas duffle bag. When the three turned to leave, Maurice made his move.

"Hey there," Maurice called out. "Aren't you three the Croc Brothers?"

"Why yes, we are. I'm Larry, and these are my brothers Andy and Bob," Larry said as the three did a little dance and ended it with a "bah bum pa bum."

"I'm Maurice," said the cat. "I just got into town. I split up from the Animal March to help a bear out of some trouble in Ocala. The plan was to meet them here in Tallahassee. I'm glad to see you're already here. Where are the rest of the animals?"

"Don't know," said Larry. "We got separated at the water park. We won an all-expense paid cruise to Cozumel, Mexico. It was great till we realized that *we* were really the entertainment and then Bob, here, overheard a steward telling a passenger we were on a one-way trip to Cozumel. A traveling crocodile circus was planning on picking us up on arrival. They were looking for a headliner act."

Andy and Bob nodded in agreement with their brother.

"What happened?" asked Maurice.

"When we got to Key West, we jumped ship. Slipped right over the side and swam ashore. Caught a ride on a tug that was pushing a barge up to the St. Marks River, just south of here. We only arrived at the Capitol a few hours ago."

"So you don't know where the Animal March is then?" Maurice asked.

"Nope. We were hoping to catch up to them when they came into town."

"Well, we've got a problem then," said Maurice. "We haven't found any animals that know where the march is. I have no idea what is going on with the legislature and the bill they are supposed to vote on. For all I know, the whole thing could be over. Right now, I'm going to talk to the pigeons. I have to find out what's going on inside the Capitol and where the Governor is."

The crocodiles followed Maurice to the wall of the Historic Capitol building and watched as he tried to get the attention of the pigeons roosting above them.

"Hey, would you mind coming down for a moment?" Maurice called up to a pair of pigeons sitting on the sill of the lowest window.

The pigeons flapped their wings. Then they turned to face away from the bobcat.

"I'm not going to touch a feather on you," Maurice yelled louder. "Hey, we need to talk."

The birds talked among themselves, totally ignoring Maurice.

"They're not going to talk to you," said a voice from directly behind the cat.

Maurice turned around to find a light gray pigeon with a bright green chest standing behind him. Its pink eyes matched its pink legs. The bird moved back and forth, then side to side as it talked.

"Because I'm a bobcat?"

"No, because *they're* government birds. They work and play right here on the grounds of the Capitol and unless you *know* somebody, or you *are* somebody important, they're not going to talk to you."

"What about you?" asked Maurice. "I need to know what's going on with the state legislature. Can you help me out?"

"No, I live across the street at the bank," the pigeon said. "I hear a few things, but not enough to help you out. I will tell you who can help. Three blocks from here is a restaurant called Carlo's. It's a place where everyone who works in the Capitol goes to lunch. The pigeons at Carlo's hear a lot, know a lot, and they really like to talk a lot. And there's an alley that runs beside the restaurant. An old cat by the name of Malware lives there. He knows every back-alley deal made in town. Swing by and check him out. You won't be disappointed."

Chapter 35
A Bad Dream

Bu Zard leaned against the wall panel of the truck. Of all the crazy things they could have done, the vulture was sure—especially after hearing the bolt drop in place on the truck door—that they had picked the worst one. They accepted a ride with a stranger knowing full well that the opossum was looking for them. Desta had told them what she overheard. The only excuse Bu Zard could come up with for why they'd taken the ride was they were all exhausted and not thinking clearly.

Tony and Sophia pushed each other, trying to get more space. Samuel's tail twitched, instead of moving back and forth, due to a lack of room, and Frieda kept mumbling something about a "bad dream" and she hoped she would "wake up any minute now."

The animals could feel the truck stop and go, probably at traffic lights. Each time the truck took off, speeding up, the animals shifted, bumping into each other.

Finally, Desta broke the silence and said what all the animals were thinking. "I don't think the boar is going to stop and let any of us out."

All the animals began talking at once.

"Not let us out?" Wanda asked, as if this had not occurred to her. "But I wanted to take the children home. Where are we? Where are we going?"

"Of course he's not going to let us out," said Frieda. "Nothing else has gone our way."

"I just want to smash all these boxes," said Samuel. "Smash right through into the front of the truck."

"Desta," said Bu Zard. "I've always heard turtles have an inner compass, an ability to know where they are." He paused, hoping he did not sound too foolish. "Can you tell where we are?"

"I don't know *where* we are, but I know the direction we're heading. North."

"North, hmmm," Bu Zard said. "At least that's the way to Tallahassee."

"You don't really think we're going to Tallahassee, do you?" asked Frieda

"Of course not, but we need a new plan," said Bu Zard. "One that starts when that door is opened."

"Please don't start the *trust me* speech," said Frieda.

"No, I'm not. I have no idea what will work or what we will be able to do when we get where we're going."

"Do you think we could move the crates and see out that small window behind the driver?" asked Samuel.

"Good idea," said Bu Zard. "The beginning of a plan. I like it."

Samuel, Bu Zard, Frieda, and Wanda tried moving the crates. The boxes were stacked on top of each other and hard to get around. The four animals pulled and pulled but could not get them to move.

"I thought this was a plant delivery truck," said Wanda. "Why are these crates so heavy?"

"Move out of the way and I'll smash them," said Samuel. "I've wanted to smash something since we climbed into this truck."

"It's too dangerous," said Wanda. "In these close quarters, and with your heavy tail, you could hurt one of us. We have children to think about."

"Wait. Lift me to the top of the crates. I can put my head down on the other side and try to see into the cab," Desta said.

"And another part of a plan comes together," said Bu Zard. Then using his wings, he lifted the little turtle to the top of the wooden crates.

Desta crawled across the very top box. A tiny sliver of light came from the window. The turtle could see very little through the small gap, so she pushed her head out of her shell as far as she could and stuck it down behind the boxes. Turning just a little this way and a little that way, she could see into the cab of the truck and right outside through the windshield. The truck was traveling on a large highway with many cars and trucks. She could see that the boar, with his two front hooves on the steering wheel, was driving the truck and seated beside him, in the passenger seat, was T.J., the opossum.

Desta sucked in a deep breath, jerked her head into her shell, and backed rapidly away from the window. She took one step too many and disappeared over the edge, landing on Samuel below.

"What happened?" asked Tony and Sophie together.

"Well, the good news is we don't have to worry about finding the other animals. I'm pretty sure we're heading to the same place," Desta told the group. "The bad news is the opossum is up front with the boar."

Chapter 36

The Gathering of Sensitive Information

Maurice led the crocodiles down Adams Street and across College Avenue to the outdoor café that the bank pigeon had told him about. The lunchtime crowd was thinning as the state workers headed back to their jobs and the lobbyists hurried back to the Capitol to find out which new laws were going to pass.

A very large group of pigeons ran back and forth across the concrete, picking up the scraps of the day, doing their jobs to clean up the streets and sidewalks. All the while, the pigeons kept up a constant chatter among themselves.

Maurice motioned for the Croc Brothers to wait while he spoke to the pigeons, but this proved to be harder than the bobcat thought. The pigeons were talking non-stop about the tidbits of information they had gathered during lunch.

"Did you hear that the Governor's secretary is retiring?" asked one pigeon.

"About time," another pigeon responded while picking up bread from under a table.

"You would think she would wait till the end of his term in office," a third pigeon chimed in.

"Got a better offer," said the first.

This set off a new round of chatter as all the pigeons surrounded the first to hear what the offer was.

Maurice could not get a word in as the pigeons gossiped back and forth over the day's lunchtime news. Music started at the other end of the restaurant as the Croc Brothers began their routine, taking advantage of the people who were left to finish their lunch.

When the bobcat looked back at the pigeons, he noticed the alley that ran down the side of the restaurant. It looked like the alley the bank pigeon had told him about, so he headed for the opening in hopes of finding the cat, Malware.

The alley was typical for a city. Trashcans sat outside the back doors that opened into the narrow passageway. At the end of the long narrow corridor, a dumpster sat with boxes stacked beside it and insects circling above it. The dumpster and the area immediately surrounding it smelled of rotten food.

Maurice walked cautiously along the wall, avoiding the center and the more highly exposed areas.

"Malware," he called tentatively and then again with his purr adding to the syllables of the alley cat's name. "Mmmaaalllware, are you here?"

A large tomcat stepped out from behind a trashcan two doors down from the part of the alley that Maurice had come from. The cat stretched and then rubbed himself against the can, scratching his side before coming all the way out in the open.

"Depends on who wants to know," replied the cat.

Maurice studied the cat for moment before he responded. "I'm looking for a cat that I've heard knows a lot about what is going on inside the Capitol. A real insider, I'm told. This cat is privy to a lot of back-alley deals and insider handshakes. His name is Malware. Do you know him by any chance?"

Now it was the cat's turn to study Maurice. The alley cat looked the bobcat over several times before asking, "What's in it for me?"

"There's not really a lot I can offer you. Except information," said Maurice. "That *is* what you crave, isn't it?"

"Maybe," purred the cat. "Tell me this information and I'll be the judge of its importance."

"A large number of animals are walking here right now from the Everglades in support of a law that is going to be voted on by the legislature, a law to help restore the Everglades. I just want to know when this vote will happen and what you've heard."

The cat laughed. "That's not going to happen. It's not going to get voted on."

"What? Why?" asked Maurice. The bobcat moved forward, getting right in the alley cat's face. "We were told by very good sources that this bill would be voted on. What has changed?"

"The Speaker, who controls the House of Representatives, is going to end the session early. He's going to table that law, move it to the next session, maybe even longer. Heard him tell that to the guy in the blue tie with yellow half-moons, standing right where you are. He made a deal to end the session early." Malware purred, licked his right paw, and then turned it over to admire his shiny claws.

"I don't understand," said Maurice. "How can they do that?"

"The man wearing the blue tie told the Speaker he could depend on his support for life. Then he gave the Speaker a necktie, a thank you gift. He's been giving away a lot of those ties lately. Anyway, as I said before, the Speaker is the boss of the House of Representatives and when he bangs his gavel, it's done. Session's over! It's the Speaker's call on how early."

"How early is it going to end?" asked Maurice.

"They're not due to be finished until midnight tomorrow. But they're ending the session at noon instead. Hey!" Malware yelled as the bobcat sprinted out of the alley. "Don't tell anyone that I told you about the deals in this alley! I don't want to lose my sources."

Maurice yelled back over his shoulder, as he ran out of the alley, "Don't worry. Just keep your ears open for anything else that's said. I'll be back."

Maurice ran back to the street-side restaurant and straight to the crocodiles. "I'm going to find my friends who're waiting in the woods and bring them here. We've got problems with our bill going before the legislature, and I need you to do something very important," said the bobcat. "Tomorrow morning, I need you to stop all the traffic coming into the Capitol."

The Croc Brothers looked at each other, then back at Maurice. Each face split into an eager grin.

Chapter 37

Plan B

Bu Zard and the other animals had been stuck in the back of the truck for over two hours. They stood together and spoke in whispers just in case the two animals in front had a way of listening in. They discussed all the possible scenarios in which to make their escape, but none of the plans would work until the truck stopped.

"We'll rush them," said Samuel who had decided to be the first one out of the truck when the gates dropped. "I'll go for the boar while the rest of you charge the opossum. If we get the jump on them we can overpower them and make our getaway."

"It may work if it's just those two," said Bu Zard. "But we need a contingency plan, in case it's *not just* those two who are out there."

"What do you have in mind?" asked Samuel. "We're not going to know how many until they open up this tin can and we look them in the eyes. I say we charge and if there are too many of them, you and Frieda fly away and go for help."

The animals worked on their escape plan until the moment they felt the truck lurch to the right and slow down abruptly. The sudden change in speed sent all but Samuel and Desta flying forward against the crates. Frieda and Bu Zard landed in the corner in a heap of legs and wings.

"Quick," said Samuel. "Put Desta on top of the crates so we can find out what's going on out there."

Bu Zard untangled himself from Frieda and got unsteadily to his feet.

The truck had slowed considerably from the previous speed and now barely moved. The brakes of the vehicle squeaked as the boar slowed again, finally bringing the truck to a complete stop.

Bu Zard lifted Desta back to the top of the crates and the turtle crawled to the small opening behind the cab. Once again, she pushed her long neck out as far as she could and stuck her head down behind the crates, twisting around to look through the window.

The boar opened his door and stepped out of the truck while the opossum dug through the glove compartment. The truck was parked in front of a row of green and white gas pumps at a small convenience store.

Desta turned her head from side to side, watching the two animals. The opossum had a small plastic card in his claw and shoved it across the seat to the boar.

The boar snatched the card up and turned to walk away, but something caused him to pause and look back at the window behind the seat.

Desta pulled her head up and back into the shell. Her heart pounded as she waited for what she thought was a very long time but, in fact, was only a few seconds. Slowly, the turtle returned to her previous position.

The boar was still there, looking at the same spot. Their eyes met and held. The boar slowly shook his head back and forth, then turned to walk away. The opossum saw none of this exchange, but instead sat stuffing the items that had fallen from the glove compartment back inside the box.

"What's going on up there?" asked Bu Zard. "Can you see what they are doing?"

Desta crawled across the top of the crate and looked down at the other animals. "They're getting gas," she said. "I'm going to stay here and watch for road signs. At least we'll know where we are."

The stop was long and twenty minutes passed before the boar started the engine and pulled away from the station.

After bracing herself with her webbed front feet against the edge of the crates, Desta slowly lowered her head back behind the boxes. The ride was not nearly as smooth as it had been on the interstate, and the truck made several sudden stops and starts. Desta's head knocked back and forth between the box and the window pane of the cab. As soon as she was steady, she twisted her head around to look inside the cab. She could see out of the window in the front of the truck easily, but trying to read road signs upside down, to figure out where they were, was a different matter. The truck picked up speed and the signs whizzed by. She had to swallow a couple of times to keep from getting sick.

When she glanced into the rearview mirror, she found that the boar was watching her. Once again, the boar slowly shook his head. The turtle didn't know what to think. She started to pull her head back into her shell when a road sign caught her attention. WEST HIGHWAY 90 was in large black letters. Desta pulled her head up and backed away from the window.

"The boar knows I'm up here," she told the animals. "He's caught me watching twice now. What should I do?"

"Let me up there," volunteered Tony. "I'll kick the window out."

"Hold on there, son," said Samuel. "We'll have our shot at them, hopefully sooner than later, but right now Desta needs to stay up there and keep us updated."

"We'll need the advantage," said Bu Zard. "Desta, as soon as you think they are about to open the back of the truck, let us know. We'll be ready."

Desta returned to her post and waited for a sign that they were getting close to their destination. After another half hour of driving, the boar suddenly turned the truck off the road they were on, drove several hundred feet, and came to a complete stop. The turtle twisted her head in every direction, looking out the front window, the side window, and across the boar to see where they were.

T.J. opened his door and dropped down from the truck cab, disappearing from Desta's view and then reappearing in front of the truck. The opossum walked up to a set of massive gates, stopped, looked up for a moment, then unlocked the gates and pulled them open.

Desta strained to watch the movements of the opossum. She twisted her head into a very odd angle and caught sight of the boar, watching her again. The boar pointed at something fluttering in the breeze on the side of the gates. It looked like a banner.

Desta pushed her nose flat against the glass of the cab and strained to see what the boar was pointing to. The opossum climbed up on the gate and pulled the banner up to reattach it. The banner read HALF-MOON ESTATES ANIMAL RELOCATION ENTRANCE. The opossum was trying to cover an older metal sign that stretched across the top of the gates.

She read, "North. Florida." The turtle backed away from the window and called down to the animals, "Hey, what's a zoo?"

"Hey, what's a zoo?"

Chapter 38

A Little Bird Told Me

Maurice finally arrived at the edge of the St. Marks Wildlife Refuge, seventeen miles south of the Capitol. He'd run the entire way without a break or a drink of water, which wasn't normal for him. He had always been a lazy cat, taking one day at a time. Now he was on a clock and it was making him very nervous. He had to make sure that the bill to help the Everglades would be voted on by the representatives and he was going to need help.

The cat dropped beside a small creek leading to the Pinhook River and took a quick drink before beginning a search for Victor and Jason. He had left them very close to the creek almost twelve hours earlier and he hoped they had stayed nearby. Maurice looked around for a bird or a squirrel that could help.

He had heard the familiar sing-song warning that had gone out when he first entered the forest and felt sure the birds were all high-tailing it out of there. Squirrels, too, for that matter. He was a bobcat, after all, and had dined on a few of their relatives.

He sniffed the area and then followed the creek downstream toward the Gulf of Mexico. A couple of times, he picked up whiffs of Jason. He smiled. That bear had learned something on this trip. He'd told the bear on their way out of Ocala to find a stream and walk in it, or back-track several times, and then jump into the water to cover his tracks. For a beginner, Jason had done okay. Maurice wasn't having an easy time tracking him.

But Maurice was a pro and he knew what to look for while tracking animals. He soon picked up very strong scents of Jason and Victor. He followed the trail another fifty feet and was about to turn away from the stream when a limb snapped behind him. Maurice froze and was preparing to jump into a nearby tree, when he heard Jason laughing.

"Told you he would fall for it," said a female voice. "That cat is getting soft since he's been hanging out with you. He's losing his instincts and becoming a kitty cat."

"How did you do that?" asked Maurice, visibly relaxing after seeing his friends. "Get behind me like that, without me hearing."

"That's our secret," said Sara. "And I have some bad news. The animals are missing."

Maurice looked at the panther and scrunched up his face. "Missing? You can't just make that many animals disappear without someone seeing . . . something. So how can they be missing? And where is Victor?"

"Let me tell you about the animals first," answered Sara. "I started doing some digging and you're right. Someone did see. I got a little birdie to tell me everything she knew. The animals were drugged and moved to a facility that is being used as a detention center. The owners are calling it a relocation center for animals that lose their homes to development."

"What? That's crazy. Where did the bird hear that information?" asked Maurice.

"Didn't just hear it. She saw it. The facility is an hour east of Tallahassee. It was called the North Florida Zoo until last year, when the new owners took over," Sara told him.

Jason motioned with his big paw and said, "That's where Victor went. When Sara told him about the animals, he took off in that direction running as fast as he could—said he was going to get his family."

"What about you, Maurice? What did you hear in Tallahassee?" asked Sara.

Maurice sat down on his haunches, shaking his head at the news he had just heard. This latest news was even worse than the information he'd gotten in Tallahassee. After a few minutes, he jumped to his feet and paced as he gave them a quick rundown of his conversation with Malware. "We need more animals," he told them. "We have to delay the end of the session and give the animals from the 'Glades time to get here. Do you think Victor can help them?"

"I don't know—the buck *seems* capable. But unless a miracle occurs," said Sara, "I don't know how you are going to hold the session an extra twelve hours or get the animals here in time."

"Don't worry. I'll stall the session. Leave it to me. I've got this," said Jason, taking off running. "Just get the animals here to make their case!"

Maurice and Sara were so surprised by the sudden departure of the bear that they had no time to stop him. All they saw was his large rear end and the mud he had used to cover the red circles slinging in all directions.

"That bear never ceases to amaze me. I spent half our trip trying to get him to speed up and now look at him," said Maurice. "I didn't know he could move that fast."

The panther has a heart

Maurice and Sara watched Jason disappear from sight.

"It's hard to imagine that he thinks he can actually do something with those red circles," said Maurice.

"He *is* a marked bear," Sara said in agreement and then turned back to the bobcat. "So what do we do now?"

"I should probably go after Jason and get back to Tallahassee."

Sara cocked her head and gave Maurice a sly grin. "Against my better judgment, I'm going to get involved. I took the liberty of asking a few animals from the Hammock to meet me. You go ahead and we'll be right behind you. Our neighborhood will meet you at the Capitol and support you."

Sara took off in a trot, headed for the pine forest.

"I knew you had a heart in there," Maurice called to the panther.

She stopped and waved a big brown paw. "Yeah, well let's keep that between us. I have to keep my reputation intact."

Maurice nodded in understanding and turned to follow Jason. He doubted Jason would make it to town, much less anywhere near the Capitol.

But the bear was the least of his worries. If the animals didn't get here soon, they wouldn't have a chance to influence the vote to save the Everglades.

Chapter 39
Time for Action

"Zoo? Where did you see that?" asked Bu Zard.

"North Florida Zoo," read Desta again. "This big, metal sign over the gate says North Florida Zoo. T.J. is hanging a new banner over it with the words—Half-Moon Estates Animal Relocation Service Entrance."

"What's a zoo, Mom?" asked Tony.

"A place for exotic animals," answered Wanda.

"Are we exotic?" asked Sophie.

"No, we are native, born and raised here," said Wanda.

"*Tch, tch, tch.* If they want exotic animals, they can go pick up the boa constrictors and pythons that are invading the Everglades," said Frieda.

"Not all animals in the zoo are exotic," said Bu Zard. "I've known injured animals that recouped in the zoo and then were set free. And they *will* take in endangered animals, and ones once kept as pets and then abandoned."

"We can always go home, can't we, Mom?" asked Sophie.

"There's a *big* fence around this place," said Desta.

The truck started moving again and Desta went back to her position behind the cab window. T.J. hadn't returned to the truck. Desta expected the boar to stop and pick up the opossum, but he didn't. The boar alone drove the animals through the gate.

The turtle pressed her face against the glass and looked out through the front window. They turned down a one-lane road with fenced enclosures on either side. Desta could see animals in all of the enclosures, some she recognized. In fact, most of them she knew. She twisted her head as far as she could to watch the animals they passed. She hurried back across the crate to tell the animals what was going on outside the truck.

"Only the boar is up front?" asked Bu Zard. "Surely we can take him."

"But where do we go?" asked Frieda. "A zoo has fences and cages, and we came through a gate. You heard Desta. The gate was locked."

The truck slowed and Desta crawled back to the window. "We're at the aviary. At least, that's what the sign says. The boar is looking at me and pointing. We've stopped. He's getting out. He's walking toward the back of the truck. . . . I can't see him anymore."

Bu Zard put his bald head against the wall of the truck and listened. The other animals crowded around him, each of them holding their breath to hear the sounds from outside the truck.

Squeeeeeek, bam, bam, jiggle, jiggle came from outside the truck and the animals pulled back in alarm.

"What's he doing?" asked Frieda. "It sounds like he's scraping the metal off the side of the truck."

"More like he's pulling the loading ramp out," said Bu Zard, moving to the back of the truck and pressing his ear to the door. "He's pulled the ramp out and is moving it into place."

That's when things started to happen fast. The animals heard the boar walk up the ramp and grab the bolt to the door. Sophie began to cry.

"*Shhh*, Sophie. Everything will be okay," Wanda whispered, trying to calm her frightened daughter.

Desta stood on the edge of the crate and looked at the animals below. Tony comforted his sister with his nose, but then he pushed her aside and turned to face the door, lowering his head at the same time.

"Hey, get me down," Desta called from the top of the crates.

But none of the animals heard her. What they heard was the unmistakable sound of a bolt being removed, then the clanking sound of the lock dropping. The doors creaked and groaned. The animals' heads pressed tightly to the door of the truck listening to the sounds coming from the outside. The back doors swung open. But they were not back to the places they agreed would give them the advantage over the boar!

The boar stared at the animals that were looking at him as if he had two heads.

Then from out of the back of the truck, Tony came running. He jumped as high and as hard as he could, aiming for the boar, but instead sailed right over the top of his head and landed on the ground behind him. Ollie turned around to look at the deer, giving the other animals the opportunity to charge, which they did—all at once—resulting in them running into each other.

Frieda and Bu Zard tumbled down the ramp and into the boar as Wanda hit them from behind. Samuel did not have a chance to get to the animal, because the first three had landed in a pile in front of him. For a few seconds, it was hard to tell the animals attacking from the animal being attacked; it was an extremely disorganized assault.

Ollie managed to move away from his would-be attackers. “Hey, hold it, hold it,” he called to the animals. “I'm here to help you, not hurt you. Just hold on a minute and we'll talk.”

Bu Zard struggled to his feet. “Help us? You locked us up for the last four hours and drove us to who-knows-where.”

“Hey, I picked you up to save you. The other plan was to just drop you in the middle of the Atlantic Ocean—and leave.”

“Squawk!!!” Frieda jumped off the ground and was about to take off, but the boar stopped her.

“No, wait! Please! Check out the boxes in the back of my truck. You might find something useful in there,” the boar said to Frieda and the rest of the group.

Bu Zard looked at the boar like he was crazy. How could they trust the boar when he had just kidnapped them and brought them to a . . . a zoo?

“Wait? Wait for what? More of your friends to get here?” asked Frieda.

“You can’t fly out of here. There is an unseen laser that will activate a trap when you fly through its beam. If you try to take off, the opossum and his employees will see you and know that I didn't lock you up. Plus, you’ll get a zap when you hit that beam. You’ve got to figure out another way. Give me just four minutes to get to the front and tell them I’ve taken care of you. That’s all I’m asking. Then you can break out or whatever.”

"You really want to help us?" asked Bu Zard, who was still very suspicious. "Why would you do that? We know T.J. was in the truck with you."

"T.J.'s bad. He's always been bad. We starting helping our employers move animals a few years ago. I was the muscle. T.J. was the front man. He would go in and convince the animals that relocation was good for them. If our employers needed an area for farming or developing, we'd go in and relocate the animals. At first, I thought I was doing the animals a favor, helping them move to a safer environment."

"Pu-lease, tell us something we can believe," said Bu Zard.

"Okay, okay, but we're standing in a place that is hundreds of acres in size with fresh water and food that is delivered daily. It sounds good in theory."

Frieda walked over to the boar and poked her wing in his nose. "So your bosses think they are going to empty the Everglades of animals and bring them here?"

"Uh huh," said the boar. "You guys made us speed up the relocation process though. We weren't quite ready for you. They couldn't have you getting the media's attention. It's not good for politicians in an election year to look like they don't care about the *environment*. And it's not good for my employers if they don't have the politicians on their side. They might not get to build the projects that are planned."

The animals stared at Ollie while Samuel moved a little closer to the boar.

"Oh, so out of the blue, you had a change of heart and have come over from the dark side," said Frieda, ever the pessimist. "And we're supposed to believe that?

"All right, you got me," said the boar. "*They*, and they meaning that crazy opossum and the man in the tie, plan to get rid of me as soon as this is over. I'm hoping you figure out how to get yourselves out of here and take me with you. Anyway, I'm all you've got, and believe me, this place is a fortress. Stay in the center areas. They've posted guards around the fences, mainly to keep people out. They really don't believe the animals can escape from the cages they've built."

Bu Zard stuck out a wing. "You got any keys to this place?"

"Check in the truck. That's all I got. Now, I need to go before they suspect me of collaborating or something. I can stall them until dark—maybe."

The animals watched the boar run down a lane that was lined with animal enclosures. They could hear the animals calling out for help as he passed by.

"You heard him," said Bu Zard. "We've got to get the animals out of the enclosures before dark."

"Help! Help! Get me down!" This last voice was coming not from the animal enclosures, but from behind them and inside the truck.

Sophie stood at the edge of the truck, pawing the floor frantically. "Desta is still on top of the crates. I can't get her down. Please help."

"The crates," said Samuel. "Didn't the boar tell us to check the crates? Get Desta off the top, because I feel like smashing something right now."

While Samuel smashed the crates in the back of the truck, Bu Zard climbed up into the cab looking for keys. There was only one—and it was in the ignition. This was a disappointment for the bird until he heard Samuel cheering in the back.

Samuel had broken all of the crates in the truck and it was like finding treasure. The truck was full of equipment from the plant nursery who owned the truck. Shovels, picks, chain saws, and even wire cutters were among the goodies found in the midst of bits of broken wood. Each of the animals grabbed a tool they could handle and headed for the aviaries, where the birds were being held.

The birds were not happy. In fact, Betty, the wood stork, began chewing Bu Zard out before he even got the gate open.

“I'll tell you one thing. I did not expect to wind up in a giant bird cage when I started this trip. I thought the trip would be a nice change in scenery and an opportunity to help our Everglades. I had no idea what I was getting myself into,” she said without so little as a breath in between her sentences.

The hawks were irate and threatened to scratch out a few eyes, but Bu Zard and Samuel managed to calm them and convince them not to attempt escape.

“Oh, we’re marching out of here all right,” said Betty. “And we’re going straight to our representatives at the Capitol. I’m going to let them know what I think about this outfit. I don’t need a new neighborhood. I’m perfectly happy with the one I have already. Humph! Trade the Everglades for . . . ” Betty stopped talking and stared across the aviary.

Bu Zard, hustled the animals along, glad to hear Betty still talking about the Capitol. “Move it, move it, we need to get on the other side of these fences.” He noticed Betty was no longer talking nor following him. He jerked around to look in the direction Betty was staring thinking he would find the opossum and the man. His heart dropped and he froze.

"Oh yeah, I forgot about them," she said.

Standing on the other side of the aviary, and supported by Della was Benson.

Chapter 40
The No Fly Zone

Bu Zard ran to Benson. The bald eagle could barely walk. Benson's wing hung uselessly at his side and he had a scrape down the side of his face. Della had to help him walk toward the vulture.

"It was a trap," Della said. "Benson was flying too low over the facility and they had a trap waiting for him."

"They knew I would follow the animals," said Benson, his pain showing noticeably by the wavering in his voice. "They told us before locking us in the aviary, that I had been flying in a no fly zone, and any animal flying in this zone was to be shot down. I was flying too low, trying to see inside, and activated their trap. They shot at me with rubber bullets to distract me and a giant net sprung in front of me as I made my second reconnaissance mission. I went down hard, wrapped up in the net and I couldn't get untangled."

Bu Zard's beak was open in disbelief. "Della, they trapped you too?"

"No, I surrendered," Della told the vulture. "When I saw Benson go down, I couldn't leave him. He's my mate for life, so I walked up to the gate and turned myself in."

Frieda and Samuel joined Bu Zard, and were ready to ask a lot of questions, but Bu Zard stopped them.

"We've got to get you out of here," he told the eagles. "We'll help you out of the aviary, but we have to free the rest of the animals. There is a nursery truck down this lane. You can rest there"

"Be careful," said Benson. "They have lookouts posted all along the fence line. They are armed with guns. And don't forget those nets. They must have some sort of sensory beacon that activates the nets around the perimeter of this facility."

"Okay, you've got to get back to our truck," said Bu Zard. "Frieda, you and Betty find out where they are holding the raccoons. They are notoriously good at breaking and entering. We'll get them out first to help us free the rest of the animals."

The raccoons, with their nimble fingers, were able to operate the equipment faster and smoother than the other animals, so they followed Bu Zard and Frieda, cutting open the wire cages, cutting off locks, and opening gates.

The outside of one large, stone building was covered in yellow jasmine and passion vine. Gutters, running along the roof line, were built to resemble the bodies of serpents, while alligator heads carved in stone jutted from the side of the building. A large sign over the door read REPTILES AND AMPHIBIANS, and below that a smaller sign read SNAKE EXHIBITS to the left.

Frieda backed away from the door and went to get Samuel. "Not happening, Bu Zard. Not in this lifetime am I *walking* into a snake house *voluntarily*."

Twenty minutes later, Bu Zard and Samuel entered the building. Lizards and frogs crawled and hopped everywhere. The cartons that had been used to transport them were dumped on the floor. The snakes, however, had been put into glass holding cages. None of the animals were happy, and the snakes had been threatening the frogs all morning.

"I know you are upset," Samuel told the snakes. "Just stay with us a little longer while we come up with a plan."

"*Ribbet!* We want to go home!" The frogs croaked in unison. "We want to go home!"

Bu Zard found the alligators, crocodiles, and turtles behind the building, swimming in a large, man-made pond with plastic logs and large, fake stones.

The old gopher tortoise crawled from underneath the roots of a fake tree and looked at the vulture, shaking his head. "I've been moved before, but I have to say, it just can't get any worse than this," he told Bu Zard. "I should have stayed with you and skipped the water park."

"I should have skipped this entire trip, *including* the march," said an irate alligator.

"Don't worry about it," Samuel told Bu Zard. "You can't make all of them happy."

Bu Zard ignored the negative remarks and pointed in the direction of the nursery truck. "We've set up a command center. Frieda and Wanda are waiting there and will give you more detail while we find the rest of the animals."

The next building was blue and white concrete and filled with water features. Inside, beavers and otters ran around in frenzied circles trying to find the escape exit.

Samuel recognized the mother and father otter family that he and Wanda had tried to talk to at the water park. He nodded as the family walked by and out the door.

"I just don't know how we got into those trucks," the mother otter said as she walked by. "Do you, Darryl?"

"No, dear," answered the father otter. "I haven't a clue."

Samuel's tail swished across the ground. "Just stay close together and away from the fences. There are guards posted and we aren't sure of their positions."

Bu Zard pointed at the adult raccoons. "I need you to stay with me. We have more animals to break out."

Bu Zard and Samuel led the raccoons through the rest of the facility. They moved cautiously down each lane peeking around corners and hoping they would not run into the opossum. They had almost completed their mission when they saw Ollie rushing toward them.

"Hey, we're putting these tools to good use," Bu Zard said. "We almost got all of the animals out of their cages." He held up a wire cutter that he had dangling on the end of his wing. "We're going to cut our way out through the fences. You can leave with us if you want."

"NO! All the exterior fences have alarms and are electrified," said Ollie. "It won't kill you but it will knock you out if you put your wing on it. I can't imagine what would happen if you use a metal tool against the current running through those fences. They've also installed an alarm system with sensors that set off traps along the fences. They've been working on this system for over a year. Don't forget that they want to keep you in here forever."

Bu Zard let the wire cutters drop to the ground. Then he kicked them in a show of frustration. He looked at the animals standing nearby. “I’m listening, if any of you have an idea,” he said.

“They know you’re breaking the animals out and they’re putting a team together to recapture you,” Ollie said. “I told T.J. that I would check on how many animals are out of the habitats. I’m not going back. He’s going to figure out that I didn’t lock you up to start with.”

Samuel’s tail moved back and forth in the sand.

“We’re going to find a way out,” said Bu Zard, sounding more confident than he actually felt. “I don’t care if it *is* a no fly zone.”

Bear in the road

It took Maurice over an hour to catch up with Jason, not because the bear was moving faster than Maurice, but because Jason was staying true to form and not recognizing any boundaries between bears and humans. Maurice had to avoid several humans with weapons that were out looking for the bear. For some reason, Jason could not grasp the concept of private property.

The first sign Maurice had that he was catching up to the bear was a set of headlights from an oncoming car veering suddenly into a ditch. When two more vehicles followed the first one into the ditch, Maurice had no doubt what the cause was and he lengthened his stride to gain on Jason. *That bear is going to get us both shot*, Maurice thought, when he finally caught sight of Jason running down the center of Nene Lane, a street in a neighborhood near downtown Tallahassee.

"Jason! Jason," Maurice called. "Hold up there! Wait for me!"

Jason slowed to a walk. He turned toward the sound of Maurice's voice.

Maurice watched more cars veer into the ditch while the drivers blew their horns at the bear standing on the center line of the road.

"What's wrong with you, Jason?" Maurice yelled at the bear when he caught up to him. "Are you trying to get killed? Follow me and get out of the middle of the road!"

Maurice headed for a band of trees in a nearby park and did not look back to see if the bear was following him. When he was well within the canopy of the trees and out of sight of the road and neighboring houses, he stopped and waited on Jason.

The big bear reluctantly followed Maurice into the trees. "I told you, I've got this," he said when he caught up with the bobcat.

"Really, Jason? You really thought you were going to make it? I bet wildlife control is on their way here right now. You ran through the middle of a family barbecue. I can't believe you made it this far."

"How else am I going to get into the center of town?" asked the bear. "I've been doing this for a long time. I know what I'm doing."

"Yeah, well, take a look at those two red spots on your big rear," Maurice said. "If we have any chance of making this whole plan work, we have to have more support. We need to wait until morning. Sara will be in town by then, and we will have some word on the Animal March and where they are. But for now, let's get as far away from here as we can because I'm sure they have a report out on you by now. They'll start looking in this area."

Jason was about to argue with Maurice, but the sound of a helicopter approaching from the south interrupted his thoughts.

"That's it," said Maurice. "They have a searchlight out for you. Stay if you want, but I'm out of here."

Maurice took off running again without listening for Jason's reply. The bear was smart enough to know the cat was right and followed him.

Chapter 41

Trust Him

All of the animals from the 'Glades were accounted for as they gathered in the center of the facility. In addition to the participants from the march, they had released animals recently relocated from other neighborhoods around the state. A covey of quail from a North Florida plantation now under development, a rattlesnake from a nearby farm, and an entire coastal community of birds and mammals removed from the Palm Coast were now part of the group.

Bu Zard stood on the back of the truck, trying to quiet the animals long enough to discuss a plan. The animals weren't cooperating and would not even consider listening to Bu Zard until Samuel bellowed his most fearsome cry.

The animals stopped talking, but hissed at the vulture.

"I have a plan," he said.

"Oh, no. Not another plan," yelled a black vulture.

"Let him talk," yelled Frieda, surprising herself with her courage addressing the animals. "Let him talk."

"I'm going for help," said Bu Zard. The idea had just come to him out of the blue. "I have to. We risk getting animals killed or maimed if we take on T.J. and his co-workers."

"How do you propose getting out of here?" asked the black vulture, Johnson.

Bu Zard glanced toward the sky where there were unseen beams that could spring a trap, a trap that could possibly cripple him or maybe even—no, he couldn't think of that. He looked back at his friends. Maybe, just maybe, if he flew hard and fast he could make it through and go for help.

"Turkey vultures are the fastest of the birds and," Bu Zard paused and looked around at all the animals, "I'm the fastest of the turkey vultures. I'm going to fly out of here tonight, right past their traps."

"You'll never come back," said a beaver in the front row.

"Yes, I will," responded Bu Zard. "I am giving you my word."

"This was your idea," said Betty, the wood stork. "How can we trust anything you come up with?"

"You can trust him, I trust him. . . . We have to trust him," yelled Frieda.

Bu Zard was thankful to hear Frieda speak up for him.

A hole in the trap

Desta sat alone inside the truck that had brought them to the relocation facility. The situation they were in was overwhelming to the turtle. She had been relieved to spot her aunt and twenty-two cousins in one of the first groups of animals to be rescued, but the facts didn't change. None of them would be safe while they were inside the facility. And now Bu Zard was planning something that could get him hurt or possibly killed.

Samuel, Frieda, and Wanda gathered around Bu Zard, obviously discussing his plan to fly out at dark. Curiosity got the better of Desta. She crawled to the edge of the truck and listened to the conversation.

The noisy crowd grew quiet. The animals agreed to rest for a while because the next day would be a long one—if they even had until the next day. When or if they did get out of this place, they still would have a two- or three-hour walk. The truck had been parked at an intersection of two lanes. The animals filled the lanes in all directions and a few even crawled under the truck. They posted guards for peace of mind, but not a single animal among them looked like they could sleep.

"Halt, stop! Who's there?" shouted a falcon that was posted at the front of the aviary. She heard something or someone move up ahead.

Desta's heart pounded. She strained to see what was going on. The boar had told them T.J. was preparing to re-cage them. A shiver ran through her body despite being in her warm shell.

Bu Zard and Samuel exchanged nervous glances.

"I'll go check this out," said Samuel. He then moved cautiously through the animals

The turtle watched the alligator crawl away. Then she looked at Bu Zard. She felt sorry for the vulture. His plan had so much potential. They were going to bring the problems of the Everglades into the public eye. But they had been stopped at every turn on this trip and now they were captives in a zoo.

Bu Zard stood as still as a statue, watching the big alligator crawl away. Then he dropped his head, shaking it back and forth as Samuel disappeared into a side lane. The red whistle still hung around Bu Zard's neck. So much had occurred in such a short time. He placed the whistle in his mouth as if he were about to blow it, to call his friend back, but instead of blowing, he let it hang limply on the side of his beak.

Frieda paced back and forth. She made several trips up the ramp and into the back of the truck. Desta decided she wanted to be with her friends and crawled down the truck ramp to be beside Bu Zard while they waited for Samuel's return.

Tony and Sophie joined Desta and Bu Zard. "I guess this could be it, Desta, so stay with us." Tony said. "I can kick hard. At least that's what Sophie says."

Desta nodded. If nothing else, she had gained a trusted friend on this trip.

Clip clop, clip clop. Desta stared hard into the distance until she could make out two shapes moving toward them. *Clip Clop, clip clop, swish, swish*. Two figures appeared in the lane: a very large alligator whose tail swished behind him and the outline of a big buck, clip-clopping alongside the gator.

"Victor!" Wanda yelled and galloped toward the two figures.

Desta let out a big sigh of relief. The turkey vulture beside her was so excited that he forgot where he was and blew the whistle over and over.

"Dad!" Tony and Sophie both shouted and rushed to greet Victor.

"Did they capture you?" asked Tony. He shoved his head into his father's neck while bucking and jumping about.

"Hold on there and I'll tell you the whole story," said Victor, as he made his way through a growing group of excited animals. "I jumped the fence. I went all around this place and the only way I could get in was to jump the fence."

"Where?" asked Bu Zard. "We didn't hear alarms go off."

"None did," said Victor. "I found an area in the southwest corner that looked like it was still being worked on."

The boar rushed up to the vulture after hearing Victor's story. "He's right! They were having trouble with the sensors in that corner. I heard them talking about it earlier today. They called for an electrician to check the electrical connections there."

"Two guards are posted near the corner," said Victor. "I had to wait until they did a changing of the guard to jump the fence."

"Wow, Dad! That was some jump. That fence is really high," said Tony.

"I'm so glad you found us, Victor," said Wanda.

"We were scared, Daddy," Sophie added.

Bu Zard's eyes grew round and he lifted his chest while turning to gaze into the direction Victor had come from.

"Then that's the hole I'm going through," said Bu Zard, talking out loud to himself. "The southwest corner, where the sensors are not working."

Only Desta heard him.

Chapter 42
A Low-flying Vulture

"What's your plan? Do you have any idea how many guards there are? How will you get back? Where are you going?" Frieda said, while trying to come up with a reason to stop Bu Zard. She did not feel as confident in Bu Zard's idea once she realized he intended to fly straight into the guards.

"It's all right, I can do this. I know I can." The vulture had been saying the same thing over and over to any animal that would listen.

Bu Zard asked Ollie and Victor to follow him to the side of the truck. Frieda and the rest of the small group of friends followed behind and anxiously stood by his side while he laid out his plan.

The vulture smoothed the sand and then found a twig to use as a pencil. He held the twig in his claw and made an X on the ground.

"Here's where we are," said Bu Zard and pointed to the X. "I'm going to have to fly low, well below their view, to get out through the corner that Victor came in. I don't want to spring the trap like Benson did earlier. Show me the route to get to the hole in the sensors."

Ollie took the twig between the tips of his rounded hooves and drew the layout of the zoo, showing Bu Zard how the lanes between the habitats connected across the facility.

"The offices are more to the right," said Victor. "I saw a large group of men and animals gathering all across the front here." The deer pointed to the detail that Ollie was drawing. "You need to bring him down this side lane, right here. You'll pass the reptile house and the bears' den. Then it's a straight line to that southwest corner."

"There's a lot of light up front, but if the sensor is still down and you stay low, they won't see you coming," Ollie added. "You really have to pick up speed in this final straightaway. In case they do take a shot at you."

Bu Zard thought he would faint. He had not thought of the possibility of being shot at. He had only considered being caught in the net.

Frieda rubbed her wings together, pacing and mumbling about the idea of rubber bullets.

Bu Zard put on what he thought was a brave face and laid a wing on Frieda's shoulder. "It's okay, old friend. This is going to work. We are getting out of here. I'll get help and be back by morning. Just make sure all the animals are ready to march out."

Frieda, still unconvinced of Bu Zard's ability to get past the traps, nodded.

Thirty minutes later, the sun was completely set when Bu Zard, flying low and fast, headed for the hole in the southwest corner.

The opossum's shot

T.J. paced the floor in the office of the relocation center.

The man in the blue tie with yellow half-moons had just arrived from Tallahassee and sat at the large desk in the room, playing with his tie and talking into a cell phone.

"Oh, yes. We have all the animals here," said the man. "No one is going to find out. Even if they do, what's the problem? This is a habitat; we're taking care of them." The man nodded absentmindedly as the person on the other end spoke in great length. "Yes, yes, I understand your concerns. We'll make sure this stays under wraps until the campaigns are over."

The man hung up and turned his attention on the opossum. "How many animals are out of their enclosures?"

"*Ahhhhmmm,*" T.J. cleared his throat. "All of them. But they can't get out of the center itself. This was, ah . . . *is* a zoo and the place is solid," T.J. assured the man. "Tight, solid, just like a prison."

"What about Ollie? You think they captured him or has he joined them?" the man asked.

T.J. did *not* want to tell his boss that Ollie was probably the reason the animals were free in the first place. He was interrupted before he had to make something up.

The radio on the desk crackled and the voice of an employee came through the little black box.

"Boss, this is Mac. You sent me to watch the animals. Can you hear me?"

"Yeah, go ahead," T.J. answered.

"Boss, I just spotted that red-headed vulture, flying low and heading for the southwest corner."

"Got it, Mac. Good eye. I'm on my way." T.J. dropped the radio and started for the door.

"Where're you going?" asked the man, dropping the tie that he'd been fiddling with and looking up in alarm.

T.J. didn't pause as he ran out the door, shouting his answer to the man, "To shoot a *buzzard*!"

T.J. made it out the door and to the first guard's station in record time. "Get ready," he told the man. "The vulture's headed this way. If he attempts to go over the fence, shoot him."

"Tranquilizers or rubber bullets?"

"Whatever you have. Just don't miss!"

One of the guards closest to the corner waved his arms frantically and yelled, "I see him. I see him coming straight down the lane."

T.J. stood on his back legs to get a better view. His first sight of Bu Zard made him think of a red-tipped rocket. The vulture was flying that fast and straight.

The guard holding the gun fired it at the vulture, barely missing him with a tranquilizer dart. The next shot was a much bigger miss because the bird had dropped suddenly, almost diving into the dirt. Then in a completely erratic move, the vulture flew straight at the guard, causing the man to drop to his knees.

T.J. watched as Bu Zard flew over his head, then up and over the fence. And just like that, the vulture was gone. They had missed their shot!

Chapter 43
What Now?

Bu Zard could not believe that the guard had actually shot at him. He had heard the *pffffff* of the first dart as it flew by, missing him only because his wing was up and not down at the exact moment it passed by. His heart had almost burst from his chest and, for a brief second, he forgot to fly. The ground rushed toward him and he flapped his wings hard to avoid smashing into the ground.

Then he saw the opossum T.J. standing by the guard and anger overwhelmed him. He flew straight at the pair, wanting to crash into them like he had crashed into the bulldozer operator on the development site. But the fence—the fence was there—right behind them. He pulled his body up and flew harder than he had ever flown in his life, up, up and into the darkness.

Bu Zard flew straight up into the night sky, and even after the lights from the ground were far behind him, he kept flying higher and higher, his heart still racing from the close call with the guard and T.J. He flew until the air from the higher altitude became cold and the oxygen was thin, and the stars became so bright they seemed to be at his wing tips. He flew higher still.

As his heart calmed and his breathing became even, thoughts of his friends filled his head. Bu Zard stopped flapping his wings. *Oh, my gosh. I have a mission*, he thought. That's when he realized he had no idea where he was, or for that matter, which direction he was heading. To make the situation even crazier, Bu Zard had promised to get help, but what help? Who or what could help them? His original plan had been to get more animals, but they would probably wind up captured too. He had to think bigger.

Bu Zard looked at the stars and, using them, he got his bearings. Now, he thought, which direction should he choose, and who was he going to go to for help? Something nagged at the back of his mind. Something that Ollie, the boar, had told them.

South! Of course! If he was going to save the animals from disappearing into that relocation center, *or zoo*, forever, he had one idea, one solution—a connection to something bigger. He just hoped they'd go along with it and help.

A bear-sitting cat

Maurice found a hiding place for himself and Jason close to a main arterial road that led to downtown Tallahassee. The two animals were exhausted after eluding the wildlife patrol. Jason had once again managed to attract unwanted and negative attention. They needed to lay low while they waited on morning to come. Sara would be here with her friends from the west coast of Florida and hopefully the Animal March would make it too.

They hid behind stacks of boxes on the loading dock of a grocery store, closed for the night. No deliveries were being made, and they took turns napping and doing guard duty. The sounds of the helicopter could be heard in the distance and, every once in a while, the intense beam of its spotlight could be seen as it searched the trees and backyards of distant neighborhoods.

They still didn't have a confirmation on the arrival time of the animals from the Everglades. Right now, they didn't even know if the Animal March *would* make it to town. He and Jason had heard nothing, and other than the disturbance that Jason had made, the Capital City was very quiet.

"Well, Sara's coming isn't she?" asked Jason. "We'll have her neighborhood from the Hammock to support the 'Glades. Won't we?"

"How much good do you think that will do us, Jason? Letting someone else's neighborhood fight for you? We need the animals from the 'Glades to show how important it is to them. *That* is what will impress the politicians. I'm going to get some rest. Tomorrow is going to be a humdinger. I can tell that for sure." Maurice curled into a ball and fell asleep immediately.

Several hours later, Maurice woke from his cat nap and stretched. He rubbed the sleep out of his eyes with his front paw and called to Jason. "Jason, hey, wake up. Some guard you are. You can't even stay awake."

Maurice walked out of the overturned box he had slept in. He licked his fur to get off the slight smell of the cabbage that had been transported in the box. Then he walked over to the box Jason had crawled into earlier that night.

"Jason," the cat said softly. He peeked around the corner of the box. That crazy bear was gone. Maurice took one more look around the loading dock and hoped the bear was just being nosey. After a few minutes of searching the area, he knew the bear had pulled a Houdini and disappeared—again. Whose idea was it for him to babysit this bear anyway?

Chapter 44
The Animals Charge the Gate

Desta was exhausted. She felt like she hadn't slept in days, and she wasn't the only animal feeling this way. Samuel had lost his temper on several occasions in the last few hours. The animals bickered and argued over what to do next. Bu Zard had left the facility, and none of them were sure of his ability to help them out. Bu Zard was good at making plans, but execution was not his strong point, and his delivery was non-existent. His plans always seemed to get bungled.

The bears, alligators, and birds of prey, particularly the owls, wanted to attack while it was dark. Many of the animals that had brought their children on the march wanted to wait for Bu Zard. The smaller animals, rodents, frogs, and even the snakes were pretty sure they could get out if all the animals charged at once.

So much arguing was going on that Samuel threatened to eat the next animal that spoke.

Desta, Tony, and Sophie climbed into the back of the truck to escape the bickering adults and come up with their own plan.

"I wish one of these animals could talk some sense into this group," said Desta.

"They're acting more like a mob and that is never good," said Tony.

A movement in the back of the truck caught their attention and they turned to find Benson standing. The eagle had rested there while trying to recover from his injuries sustained by the traps used to capture him.

"I guess I'll give it a try," Benson said. "You're right. We need to calm them to give Bu Zard a chance to get help. I'll talk to them." Then he brushed his good wing across Desta's head. "Let's see if we can talk some sense into the group, shall we?"

Benson was the deciding factor. The bald eagle went to the back of the truck. With Desta, Tony, and Sophie standing behind him, he raised his one good wing to get the animals' attention.

"Listen, listen to me. They are heavily armed," he said. "We have only ourselves. We have to give Bu Zard a chance. It's the only way we might *all* get out alive and unharmed. We will be ready though. If Bu Zard's plan doesn't work or he's not here by morning, we'll have to do something."

The sight of the injured eagle quieted the other animals. Desta watched Benson turn and hobble back into the truck. Benson had reminded the animals that injury was a reality if they fought their way out.

The small turtle turned to Tony and Sophie. "I'm pretty scared," she told them. "I don't want to stay in here forever."

"Let's stick together—no matter what," said Tony.

"I'm staying with Mom and Dad," said Sophie.

"We're not leaving Desta," said Tony.

Desta smiled. She knew she had a friend for life.

The next few hours proved to be nerve-racking for Desta and her friends. A heavy spring fog formed during the night, casting an eerie look to the bleak facility. When the animals saw the first signs of light, they stood up, stretched, and prepared themselves for the day to come.

"Gather up!" Samuel yelled from the back of the truck. "We need to make final plans for leaving this facility. Remember what we've talked about; there are hundreds of us and very few of them. Hopefully, Bu Zard will be there to meet us."

Desta made sure to stay with Tony and Sophie when they went to find their mom and dad. The group then joined Samuel as he crawled down from the truck and went to the front of the animals to lead them.

Benson, with Della's help, limped down the ramp on the back of the truck and went to stand beside Samuel, nodding to Desta when he saw her climb onto Samuel's back.

Most of the animals, Desta included, kept looking up, hoping Bu Zard would miraculously appear. The sun climbed higher into the sky and a murmur rippled through the crowd. The vulture had not returned. A decision must be made. Wait longer or go without Bu Zard.

The falcon that had been posted as guard the night before ended their dilemma of what to do. "They are getting their group together near the front gates," she told Samuel.

"How many?" asked Samuel.

"I couldn't tell. I just saw a lot of activity close to where I was positioned."

Samuel looked at the sky once again, hesitated for a moment, and then signaled the animals to move. The group moved forward in unison. They were ready for a fight with the opossum and appeared fearless as they marched forward.

"Stay together!"

"There are more of us!"

"USA, USA! Together we are strong!"

The animals called out encouragements from one to another. They filled every lane as they moved toward the front gates of the facility.

The closer the Animal March got to the gate, the more of their opposition became visible. The animals could now see who they would have to contend with to leave. There were at least four or five opossum, ten pigs and, mixed in with the animals, were humans—a lot of humans. T.J. and the man wearing the blue tie with yellow half-moons stood side-by-side.

When they were within a hundred feet of the gate, the humans and some of the pigs raised weapons and aimed at the animals.

Ollie approached Samuel. "Let me talk to them."

"If you think they'll listen, go ahead."

"We're coming through!" yelled Ollie.

"Ollie, have you lost your mind?" T.J. yelled. "Our employer will have your hide if you don't stop this nonsense. The animals will be happy here. It's true, we weren't totally ready for them, but we didn't have a lot of time to prepare. Soon this will be paradise and the animals will have everything."

"Except our freedom and our 'Glades," said Samuel. "No, thanks. We'll pass, and we are leaving even if we have to fight our way out."

In spite of the words that Samuel delivered, T.J.'s bunch did not lower their weapons or back away. They were ready to fire on the animals.

A shadow from overhead swept across the ground, causing everyone to look up. Bu Zard circled once high above the facility, high enough to stay away from the beams. Then he landed at the front gate and knocked.

Samuel looked back and forth from Victor to Benson. What was Bu Zard doing?

T.J. looked at the man, then back to the group of animals. "Hold your positions," he yelled.

The knocking continued.

"Well, don't just stand there. Let him in," said the man.

T.J. opened a small side door beside the gate.

Bu Zard walked in past the opossum and man, nodded to them, and said, "My friends are right behind me. Please, let them in. They just can't wait to see the accommodations."

The opossum was completely confused and looked to the man once again.

The vulture joined his friends, then turned to face T.J. with the rest of the group. "Help is almost here," he said low enough that only Desta, Frieda, and Samuel could hear him.

"Thank goodness," said Frieda.

"Hold your positions," shouted Bu Zard.

"I'm opening the gate," said Ollie. "It's the only way to get out."

"No! Wait! I've got help coming," Bu Zard said, trying to stop the boar.

But Ollie was already running.

Bu Zard could only watch as T.J. ordered his men to stop the boar. The first tranquilizer darts bounced off the boar's thick hide. He almost made it to the gate when a dart hit him right between the eyes. He took several more steps and collapsed on the ground.

At the sight of Ollie falling to the ground, some of the animals took steps back in retreat, a few snakes surged forward thinking they could make the gate, and the younger animals made distressful noises.

Victor told his family to get behind him. Tony pushed his sister away and stepped up with his dad and mom, while Desta pulled her head back into her shell just in case a stray tranquilizer dart might fly her way.

An animal from behind Bu Zard shouted, "Look at the door."

The animals, including T.J., watched as the new arrivals walked in the door, which T.J. had left opened.

Frieda was the first to voice her indignation. "Bu Zard, you've got to be kidding. That's all the help you brought? The flamingos? We're sunk."

The diva flamingos came through the gate one-by-one, as if they were walking onto a stage, and joined the band of animals. The animals took up all of the courtyard and every lane or sidewalk leading to the gate.

Kandee waved at everyone. Then she wrapped her wings around Bu Zard's neck. "We're here, just like you asked."

As soon as Rome, Lola, and Raquel arrived inside the relocation facility, they too joined Kandee in waving and blowing kisses.

"Bu Zard, what's going on here?" asked Samuel

"Wait for it. . . . " said Bu Zard, low enough that only Samuel and Frieda could hear.

"They're your backup. This is good, really good," said T.J. The opossum turned to the man, laughing hysterically. He issued an order to his employees. "Whoever moves in this direction, tranquilize them. We'll get the vet in later."

Wop! Wop! Wop! Wop! The noise came from behind the trees and moved quickly toward the group. *Wop! Wop! Wop!* got louder and louder.

"Smile everyone," shouted Kandee. "You're on TV."

From over the trees, two helicopters came into view. Each of the aircraft carried a camera crew. Cameras were pointed down at the animals as the helicopters circled high above the center. They got the whole scene for the five o'clock news.

The flamingos waved and blew kisses. They jumped up and down as the cameras recorded everything.

"I remembered what Ollie told us when he set us free," said Bu Zard. "His bosses could not afford to have the media involved in an election year. Then I remembered: the Miami flamingos have the connections—all the connections. I met with their media friends all through the night; the media is very interested in this place."

"And, waa-laa! Here we are to help our friends," said Kandee.

The men and animals that had supported T.J. immediately dropped their tranquilizer guns and ran to open the gate. As the gates opened, the animals watched a line of trucks with satellite dishes drive toward the center. Reporters and camera men jumped out of their vehicles and ran to the animals.

The man wearing the blue tie with yellow half-moons disappeared.

Frieda's beak still hung open, but she managed to put her wings around Kandee and give her a big hug.

Chapter 45

To the Governor's Office

In the early morning light, Maurice looked like any other stray city cat out scrounging for breakfast. Except that he was, once again, chasing a crazy bear. Maurice did not have time for this. He needed to be at the Capitol. He had made arrangements with Sara and had asked the Croc Brothers to help him hold up the Speaker's timetable. All of this could be in jeopardy if the bear did not control himself. Maurice tracked Jason's scent for several blocks, without seeing much traffic or having human contact.

By the time he got within sight of the Capitol, traffic was picking up and he had to be careful picking his way through the heavily congested streets of the city. It took him twice as long to go half the distance. So it was a little after eight thirty in the morning when he arrived a few streets from the Capitol.

The first thing Maurice noticed as he got closer to the Capitol was that traffic had slowed to a standstill and was not moving in any direction. He watched the light in front of the Historic Capitol change from red to green to red again, and the same cars sat still in the street. Horns blew and people got out of their cars to see what was going on in front of the old state Capitol.

Maurice crossed Apalachee Parkway by running between the cars that blocked the roadway. Fumes from the exhausts of all the cars mingled with smells of breakfast from the diners that were open on both sides of the divided road.

Maurice made it to Monroe Street where the object of the hold-up seemed to be located. Most of the cars he passed were empty; the drivers had left their vehicles in the middle of the road and had continued on foot to the roadblock ahead.

As Maurice got closer to the commotion in the street, he could here chants and yelling coming from near the Capitol. Finally, he could see what was causing the traffic to back up. Larry, Andy, and Bob had chained themselves to parking meters and refused to move.

Maurice moved cautiously between the legs of the people standing around the Croc Brothers. As he got closer to the circle, he saw that the pigeons from the café were also there, along with Malware the cat. Signs were placed all around the animals. SAVE OUR EVERGLADES and PROTECT OUR WATER were just some of the words that Maurice could read.

"Uh, what are you doing?" Maurice asked Larry when he got to the center of the roadblock.

"Just what you asked us to do," answered Larry. "We're holding up the meeting. The representatives will have trouble getting here this morning. According to our flying friends, traffic is backed up on every street leading to downtown all the way to Interstate 10."

"The police will haul you away," said Maurice.

"That's why the chains," Larry said. "We've chained ourselves to the fire hydrants and parking meters on both sides of the road. It's a sit-in. A very kind lady told me about it. She said sit tight and she would be back with a few hundred of her closest friends."

Maurice looked over at Malware the alley cat, who waved and nodded back.

"Well, I guess it will slow the representatives down some," said Maurice and then asked. "Have you seen a black bear?"

"Oh, most definitely," answered Larry. "He was on his way to see the Governor."

Maurice shook his head in frustration. "You're kidding," he said. "Okay, I'll be back. I've got to find the bear and stop him from getting us all in bigger trouble than we already are." The cat eyed the Croc Brothers and their chains as he said this.

Maurice ran past the protesting animals and raced across the lawn of the Historic Capitol building and around to the more modern buildings that housed the executive and legislative branches. He slowed as he approached the Capitol steps. Guards stood in front of the building and were listening to a two-way radio.

Maurice flattened himself against the wall quickly.

"Copy that," one guard said. Then he turned to his co-worker. "We've got a bear loose inside the Capitol."

"Probably one of the protesters that got away from the group chained out front," said the second guard.

"No, this bear is marked. He's a threat. We're keeping the Governor in a secure location inside the Capitol—his office. You stay here and watch the front and don't let any more animals into the building," the guard said.

"Gotcha."

Maurice looked around for an alternative way in. He had to get to Jason quickly. The guards would shoot to kill a marked bear.

Maurice eased around the guards staying out of sight by hiding in the bushes. He decided to check on the other side of the building for a better way in. At the back of the building, Maurice could only see one old guard on duty and he was reading the morning newspaper. It looked like this entrance was at a lower level than the front and it was for employees.

A state employee, on her way into work, walked past the guard and to the elevator. “Morning Mark,” she called to the guard. “What’s going on here? I had to walk from my apartment this morning.”

“Oh, some animals up from the Everglades are blocking the roads. We’ll get it cleaned up in a bit.”

The lady pushed the button for the elevator at the same time her cell phone rang. She struggled with her purse and pulled the cell phone out as the elevator door opened in front of her. While she answered, Maurice took the opportunity to run through the elevator’s open door.

“Nice kitty cat,” she said. Then, putting her phone on her shoulder, she told the elevator attendant, “Governor’s office.”

The elderly attendant looked down at Maurice and then up at the lady who was once again talking on the phone. “That’s not a kitty cat,” he said. He pushed the button for the Governor’s floor.

The elevator ride to the first floor was short and the door opened seconds after the operator pushed the button for the

“That’s not a kitty cat.”

Governor's office. Maurice ran past the lady as she stepped out into the foyer beside the rotunda of the Capitol.

"Here kitty, kitty," she called. Then she returned to her conversation on the cell phone. "Mom I've got to go. I'm delivering some papers to the Governor and I'll call you tonight when I get through with work. It's the last day of the session and I plan on getting out of town early."

Maurice ran along the corridors and into the waiting room outside the Governor's office. A large sofa sat against the wall and Maurice dove under it just as the lady from the elevator walked into the room. He could see her legs and shoes as she approached the sofa. When he saw her hand appear on the floor, he knew he was about to be caught. He wondered what the guards would do to a bobcat in the Governor's office and prepared himself to pounce on the lady. But a door from across the room opened and the hand disappeared.

"Elaine, great, you're here. The Governor needs those papers, pronto. He needs to be read up on everything happening before he can approve any of the bills," a voice said from inside the room.

Elaine turned to walk into the Governor's office, leaving Maurice under the couch.

Phew, thought Maurice. *That was a close one.* He had to think quickly about his next move. He crawled out from under the sofa and watched as the Governor's assistant turned away from Elaine to lead her into the inner office. He had to find the bear, but he could probably get better information about the legislative session from the Governor's office. He could probably find out what the plans were for Jason there, too. What should he do? Maurice did not hesitate another second. He dashed behind Elaine and managed to squeeze through the door into the Governor's office right before it closed.

Chapter 46
Marching to the Capitol

Bu Zard and Frieda linked wings with the flamingos and walked straight toward the gate of the relocation facility. When they reached Ollie, they stopped and with cameras rolling and all eyes on them, Frieda pulled the tranquilizing dart from between the boar's eyes with her beak.

"Let's get a gurney over here and put him into one of these vans," Bu Zard said while looking at T.J.

When Samuel passed T.J., he made it a point to get very close to the opossum. "Nothing had better happen to Ollie. A lot of cameras are out there, getting this on film. I'm sure your employers do not want to be known as unfriendly."

As soon as Bu Zard stepped through the front gates of the relocation facility, reporters crowded around him, and pushed their microphones into his face.

"Over here, Bu Zard," someone shouted.

"Bu Zard, question please. Over here," said another reporter.

Bu Zard held up his wings and acted as spokesperson.

"We are the *United Species of Animals*. We are marching on the Capitol of the State of Florida to let our representatives know we're not happy with choices being made that affect our way of living. There are a lot of us and together we are making our voices heard."

The animals cheered and surged forward. The chanting started at the back of the crowd and was quickly repeated throughout the group. "Save our water! Save our 'Glades! Save our species!"

The reporter from the Miami news station and his cameraman followed the group as they marched toward the Capitol. "As you can see, Katie, the animals are continuing with their historic march across the state of Florida. It's becoming quite the movement. Our sources inside Tallahassee tell me that animals are already in the Capitol City that have chained themselves together and are shutting down the main arterial streets of the city."

"Yes, Sam, we have been getting reports all morning from Tallahassee," the news anchor said. "The animals are there specifically to convince the representatives to vote yes on a bill to clean up the water flowing into the Everglades and to restrict development in the immediate area. We've heard conflicting reports on whether this bill will be voted on in this session. There have been rumors that the session would end early and this bill could be postponed."

The reporter turned to Bu Zard, shoving the microphone into his face. "Do you think you will make it to the Capitol in time?" he asked.

"We've come this far to make ourselves heard. I don't think the animals are going to back down now. Besides, it *will not* look good in an election year to put off this many animals."

"Did you hear that Katie? The animals are challenging the politicians," the reporter told the news anchor. "It looks like the elected representatives might need to stick around and hear what this group has to say."

Bu Zard listened as the reporter spoke to his news station. "Oh no, they won't put us off," he told Frieda. "They will have to acknowledge our presence. That is certain."

A bear of a problem

Back at the Capitol, Maurice had hidden himself between a file cabinet and the wall. He could hear the Governor speaking loudly on the phone in the other room. Elaine waited patiently outside the door in the assistant's office.

"What do you mean the *United Species of Animals* is descending on the town? I thought you said they were not that serious. They were supposedly at a water park or something in Orlando," the Governor yelled, sounding confused and irate. "What do you mean a relocation facility? Do you realize this is an election year? I don't want to be involved in anything that'll come back to bite me. Is that clear? No we are *not* ending the session early. I don't care what you were promised."

Maurice heard the phone slam down and then a buzzer from on top of the Governor's assistant's desk. Maurice pressed himself as close to the wall as possible not wanting the assistant to see his hiding spot on the other side of the desk. He could see the assistant's hand reach across the desk and hit the intercom button.

"Yes, sir."

"Find out what is going on out there. Send someone to find out what the animals are demanding! I'm not going to let this mess up my campaign," the Governor yelled. "Oh, and I was just informed that there's a bear and a panther in the legislative wing. Get them out of there and find someone to explain this mess to me!"

"Yes, sir, and I'll turn on the TV for you. The news media is covering the walk," said the aide. "Oh, and sir, Elaine is here with yesterday's legislation. What—"

"Send her in and get me those demands from the animals. We've got to throw them a bone. You know, give them *something* to get rid of them."

The Governor hung up on the aide as Elaine entered the room and put the papers down on the desk. She was out in less than four seconds and headed for the door.

"See you later," the aide said to her as he walked into the Governor's office, leaving Elaine alone in the outer office.

Elaine hurried across the room and yanked the door open, almost running to the elevator. Maurice ran right behind her.

The same elevator attendant from Maurice's earlier ride was inside the elevator.

"Legislative floor," said Elaine. As she turned around in the elevator, she looked down at Maurice sitting in the corner. "You're not supposed to be here. It's a good thing the Governor didn't see you. He would have shot us both," she told the bobcat. Then she turned to the attendant. "Can you take him back down and walk him out of the building?"

The man nodded and shook his finger at the cat. But as soon as the door of the elevator opened, Maurice ran out and hurried for the doors leading to the legislative branch of the state. His timing was perfect. The doors into the House of Representatives' chambers opened just as he got there. Elaine was right behind him.

"Stop that cat," she yelled at the representatives coming from the room.

But Maurice had already slipped through the doors. *It's a good day to be a bobcat*, he thought as he ran toward the front of the auditorium. He was halfway down the aisle before he noticed the podium on a raised stage in front of him. The sight of a bear and panther in front of him caused him to stop so quickly that his back legs overran his front legs.

Jason stood in front of the representatives at the podium, a gavel hanging from his mouth. Sara was at the side of the podium and had the Speaker of the House boxed in by the wall. All of the members on the floor were standing in complete shock as they watched the two animals take control of the House of Representatives.

Flashes went off across the room, like a sky of shooting stars, as the members who thought the situation was picture-worthy snapped shots with their cell phones.

Maurice noticed Capitol guards running across the viewing area high above the chambers. Each guard carried a tranquilizer gun and was finding a position that would allow a good view and shot of the podium. *Oh, this is not good*, thought the bobcat. He could leave now and save himself or get taken out with Jason. He did not want a red spot painted on his rear. That was one thing he knew for certain.

Several of the representatives took pictures of Maurice. A tall lady with dark blue heels leaned down to pet the bobcat. A silk scarf, a blue one with a yellow half-moon pattern imprinted throughout, was tied around her neck. The representative beside her wore a necktie cut from the same material. Looking around, the bobcat saw that the pattern was displayed by many of the people present.

Maurice thought back to the conversation he had with the alley cat. Malware had said that an HM Consolidated Enterprises employee was giving away ties in the alley. It looked like scarves were also given away. The bobcat began to worry; if HM Consolidated had gotten to the representatives in the legislature first, then how would they ever convince them to vote for the Everglade's bill?

Here goes nothing, Maurice thought. Without further hesitation, he sprinted down the steps and jumped on the stage with Jason.

"Jason, what are you doing?" Maurice asked.

The bear dropped the gavel and answered Maurice, "I told you, I have this. I've got the gavel. They can't end the session without the gavel. I'm giving the rest of the animals time to get here."

Sara let out a high-pitched panther scream that sent more of the representatives running from the room.

"I'm not ending the session early," the Speaker cried. "I've already told you. The Governor wants the vote to happen. If you'll just give me my podium, we can get on with the vote."

"Sara, Jason, we've got to get out of here. This is not looking good. Look up in the viewing area."

"I'm not leaving until the animals get here," said Jason.

"What do you want?" asked the Speaker who was sliding down the wall to get away from the panther. "I'm here to listen. That whole relocation thing was just a misunderstanding. I promise."

A side door opened and the Governor's aide ran across the stage. "The Governor wants to know what you're asking for," he said. He pushed a piece of paper toward the bear. "Here, write down your requests. The Governor is open to suggestions."

Jason knocked a pen to the ground and Maurice hastily scribbled out the animals' requests. He ended his list with a pardon for Jason and shoved it across the floor to the aide.

"Okay." said the aide. "Now, follow me out of here. I'm going to give you safe passage to the street, but you have to promise not to re-enter the building. The guards will have orders to tranquilize you if you do."

"I promise," purred Maurice. Then he glared at Jason and Sara until they both agreed to leave the building peacefully.

"You wanted me to get involved," Sara said with an indignant tone, as they followed the aide out of the building. "I thought I did just that."

Chapter 47

Together We Are Strong

Bu Zard's group made it into Tallahassee by one o-clock that afternoon. The roads were being cleared by a police escort sent by the Governor's office. The group arrived in town amid cheers and chants as people pulled their vehicles over to let the animal pass. The march was no longer just the animals from the Everglades. The animals were being joined by humans.

"They are with us on this, Frieda. Look at the people who are here in support of our Everglades." Bu Zard held his bald red head very high as he walked into town. He had made it all the way and, to his knowledge, he had made it with all of the animals. He looked at Frieda and nodded at the crowds.

"You were right about getting the attention of the people, Bu Zard," said Frieda. "Together we *are* strong!"

Samuel, with Desta riding on his back, followed closely behind Bu Zard. Tony was right beside them.

"I can't believe we made it," Tony shouted as he pranced sideways for a moment.

Desta could believe it. They had stuck together. Even with all their differences, they had stayed united.

The closer they got to the Capitol, the more animals joined them. Sara's group from the Hammock joined the walk as

Bu Zard led the animals down the center of Monroe Street to the front of the Old Historic Capitol.

Victor recognized the coyote leader standing on the sidewalk. The coyote's front leg was in a sling. The coyote nodded as Victor walked by and the big buck returned the nod.

"Who's that?" Tony asked his dad.

"Long story, son. Remind me to tell you one day."

The flamingos waved and blew kisses all the way into to town, pausing only to have their pictures taken.

Maurice and Jason were ecstatic when the Animal March came into view and they ran to join the animals for the last few steps of the walk.

As soon as they reached the front of the Capitol, the Croc Brothers led them in a chant that could be heard all the way to the Governor's office.

"This is it," Bu Zard told Samuel. "This is our state government and our concerns will be heard today."

Benson urged Della to fly above the crowd. The sight of the bald eagle over the buildings brought more cheers from the animals and their human supporters.

The television crews filmed the circling eagle for the news. Then all turned their attention to the Capitol steps as the Governor had chosen this moment to make his appearance.

The crowd parted as Bu Zard led his small group toward the Capitol steps. "We need to get close to the front when the Governor speaks. This is the chance of a lifetime."

"Welcome, welcome, animals from around the great state of Florida," the Governor's voice boomed from the podium. A high-pitched screech emitted from the microphone and the Governor paused while his sound crew adjusted it.

"Hurry," said Bu Zard. "We're almost to the front!"

"Okay, let's try this again," said the Governor as he adjusted the height of the microphone. "All right, now, there. I think we have it. Welcome!"

The animals cheered and Bu Zard heard the Croc Brothers chanting from somewhere in the crowd. "Save our water. Save our 'Glades."

"Yes, yes, of course, that is why we are here today, to let the great wheels of the system work," said the Governor. "But before we talk about our great system of laws, I've got Governor's business to take care of. I hear we have a renegade bear in our mist that needs a pardon." The Governor paused. "Is Jason the bear here? Jason, the bear of West Hill, Ocala National Forest. Are you in the audience?"

Near the front and across the way from Bu Zard's group, Maurice patted Jason on the side, and then gave him a little push. "You're up, big guy. Get on up there and get your pardon."

While Maurice watched the bear move through the crowd, a set of antlers caught his attention. Victor had made it! Maurice slipped into the crowd to get to the buck.

Jason moved around animals and walked up the Capitol steps to the landing where the Governor and a team of wildlife control officers waited.

"Jason, the Governor's office has prepared this conditional pardon for you, of which the conditions are simple. We will pardon your past crimes and acts against the people and you will stop all forays into the cities of the state of Florida. We are giving you a clean slate, in other words. But you must work with us. Is this clear?"

Bu Zard still could not see what was going on up front. His group struggled to get through all of the animals already gathered at the Capitol. As he and his friends began to get noticed, the animals moved aside, opening a path for Bu Zard to get closer to the Governor.

"All right, by the power invested in me by the people and animals of the State of Florida, I am here to pardon you. Officers, you may strike out the marks that have been placed against Jason the bear," the Governor said as he stepped back.

Bu Zard could finally see the top of the steps and Jason. He watched as the wildlife officers took out a can of red paint and painted a line through each of the round circles on the bear's backside: one slash mark through the center of each circle. Then Jason stood on his back legs and bowed to the audience. Elda and her cubs ran to join him at the top of the stage, and hugs and kisses were passed back and forth between mother and son while the mother bear thanked the Governor over and over.

The four flamingos had worked their way to the podium and stood behind the Governor and Jason. The pink birds were once again wearing their tiaras and boas. Rome had made an addition to her wardrobe; wrapped inside her boa was a flying squirrel snuggled in the folds and pulled close to the flamingo's feathered chest. The four blew kisses to the audience and turned in such a way as to assure their best sides were available for pictures.

Bu Zard yelled to Samuel, "Just a little closer. We're almost there. Can you see yet?"

Desta edged up closer to the head of the big gator and held tight as they made their way to the front of the crowd.

Maurice joined Bu Zard's group and helped them to press forward.

"Good to see you, Maurice," Victor told the bobcat.

"We're going to have a talk about you leaving me with that bear. It's been one heck of day," Maurice said. "Glad you found the wife and kids."

The Governor went back to the podium to resume his speech. "Now we can address our business at hand. The representatives in the current legislative session are getting ready to vote on Bill 874, which addresses the natural resources in our state as well as the plight of the Everglades."

The animals cheered again, "Save our Everglades. Save our water."

"Of course, there is nothing I would like better than to be the Governor that restores the Everglades, but there are a lot of considerations we, as the leaders of the state, need to take into account. We have deficits in our budgets and a rough economy, just to mention a few things that we must consider when we are making these tough decisions."

Bu Zard and his group finally made it to the front, as close to the Governor as possible. Frieda squeezed in close to Bu Zard and made room for Wanda and Victor to stand beside them. Tony and Sophie came around to stand by their mother and father. They were close enough to see the Governor's head sticking up from behind the large podium at the top of the Capitol steps.

"What's he saying?" asked Frieda. "Is he for this or not?"

"Animals and people," continued the Governor. "We appreciate the turnout *and* that you came as a group to exercise your right to *freedom of speech.*"

The Governor stepped out from behind the podium and Bu Zard could now see all of him. At that moment, the words coming out of the Governor's mouth all ran together and began to sound like, "Blah, blah, blah, blah, blah."

All eyes were on the Governor as he raised his hands over his head. The tie around his neck fluttered in the wind and Bu Zard's entire group could now see the yellow half-moons standing out on the dark blue necktie.

Wanda gasped and Tony yelled, "Look at that. Look at his tie."

"I guess they gave him one too," said Maurice. "It's not looking good for the Everglades right now."

The Governor continued his speech. "We have arranged audio from inside the session. You'll be able to hear the roll call and votes made by the representatives. You will find the process very educational."

"What if they don't vote for it?" asked Desta. "What then? Are we going to lose our homes?"

Bu Zard stood still and watched the Governor walk across the steps of the Capitol and back into the building. The intercom from inside the Capitol's rotunda was now hooked up and the animals could hear as the Speaker called for the first vote.

As each vote was cast, it became more and more clear to the animals that their bill would not pass that day. Many looked around in disbelief. But, from the back of the crowd, a chant started. At first, it was low and the group up front could not hear what was being said.

"We want Bu Zard." The crowd chanted louder. "We want Bu Zard."

Frieda turned to her friend and placed her wings on both sides of Bu Zard's head. "They want you Bu Zard. *You* are the influential animal now. They want you!"

Once again, it became clear, just as it had in the Everglades that day not so long ago. It was all crystal clear. They were strong when they were united.

Bu Zard flew to the top of the podium and the crowd went wild. He held his wings in the air, waiting for the chance to speak.

"Speech, Bu Zard. Speech."

"USA, USA. Save our Everglades."

Bu Zard was about to speak when a loud piercing sound came from the microphone. Bu Zard looked around and caught sight of the man in the blue tie with yellow half-moons and the opossum unplugging the cord to the sound system. He started to yell out, but Samuel and Maurice were already heading in their direction.

The crowd still chanted, "Bu Zard, speech! Bu Zard, speech!"

A commotion broke out in the corner by the equipment, which quieted the crowd for a moment. The animals standing in the area scattered in all directions.

The man twisted around and tried to push his way through the crowd. The opossum was hidden by the movement of the animals.

"Hey, it's the opossum that locked us up!" shouted a bear near the uproar.

"It's the man! Get him!" animals shouted.

From the top of the podium, Bu Zard watched the man run out of the area, the skinny tail of the opossum right behind him. In the corner, Maurice plugged the cord to the microphone back into the sound equipment. Samuel was right beside the bobcat, blocking the area from any more intrusions from the man or the opossum.

When Samuel turned toward Bu Zard, the vulture knew there wouldn't be any more problems today. Hanging out of the big gator's mouth were the remains of a blue tie with yellow half-moons.

Maurice raised his paw and pointed at the sky with one claw, giving the all clear sign.

Bu Zard tested the microphone by tapping his wing on it. The crowd went wild again.

"Speech, speech."

"USA! *United Species of Animals!*"

"Thank you, thank you for being here and supporting our plan to clean up the Everglades," said Bu Zard. "There is something everyone should know. We didn't win today, but we didn't lose either. We've learned that, despite our differences, we can work together and we can keep fighting for our Everglades. This is not the end of our mission. We'll come back."

“This is not the end of our mission.
We’ll come back.”

The crowd went wild again, cheering, and yelling support.

Bu Zard looked down at his friends, Samuel, Frieda, Desta, Maurice, Victor and Wanda with their two young ones. They had supported him the entire way. Without them, he would not have made it to the Capitol. He waved for his friends to join him at the podium.

"We'll come back every year until they hear us. We'll bring more and more animals with us from every part of the state. This Governor won't be here forever and neither will the representatives. But *we* will! And our children will! We are the *United Species of Animals* and we'll come back until they get the point."

Epilogue

The animals were disappointed that year. The bill narrowly failed in the legislature. It took two more years before the animals were able to get the votes they needed to regulate the development around the Everglades and force a mandatory purification of the water act. The Governor was re-elected and helped get the bill passed but negotiated the deal after agreeing to allow oil drilling deep in the heart of the Everglades.

Bu Zard led the group back to Tallahassee two more times and was able to get national support. He eventually became a lobbyist, representing all the animals of the state. He now spends most of his time at the Capitol, meeting with representatives. He does not give away neckties, but he does give free eco-tours of the Everglades to anyone interested in the natural resources of the state.

Frieda is still Bu Zard's assistant and best friend. She follows him to Tallahassee every year during the legislative session. She continues to complain and promises that every year is her last, but she has established a small home away from home in St. Marks, a small town by the coast. She flies down every afternoon during the session, and the coastal community helps her to cope with her homesickness.

Samuel never returned to Tallahassee again. He went back to the Everglades and is very rarely seen. He does tell the story of his trip with the Animal March to his grandchildren, the ones who have enough courage to get close to the enormous alligator.

Desta teaches at the local turtle school and is an expert on marsupials from all over the world. She and Tony have remained friends and have made several more marches to the Capitol together.

Tony is attending Deer Tech and has a full scholarship in track and field, excelling in high jump. He's not sure of what he wants to study. Sophie is majoring in zoology and has a minor in sociology. She plans to work at a relocation facility for animals in the mid-west.

Wanda and *Victor* have five other children, in addition to Tony and Sophie, and they spend most of their days trying to figure out how they will send them all to college.

Maurice works for the Department of Animal Justice in probation for wayward animals. He also negotiates with animals that are habitual nuisances to human society. He has an eighty percent success record rehabbing the offenders.

Jason is in the twenty percent that Maurice could not rehabilitate. The bear returned to the city and was captured several more times. He now has two more slashes added over his red marks, which actually makes them Xs. This negates his pardon and he is currently on the wanted list.

The *Croc Brothers* were given a variety show which lasted one season. After having a dismal tour on the road, they returned to Hollywood and managed to get a deal for a talk show. They are now syndicated and seen around the world every day.

The flamingos were an overnight sensation and became quite popular, appearing in all the gossip magazines. *Kandee* and *Rome* were given their own reality series which caused a falling out with *Lola* and *Raquel*. Raquel has been able to get several bit parts in a show on the Animal Channel and Lola married a flamingo dancer from Argentina.

Sara travels the country and joins all animal movements concerning the environment. She says she is no longer content with sitting on the sidelines. She has been spotted with some very radical groups and has been arrested in several unauthorized sit-ins.

T.J. has new employment, sweeping floors for a pet shop in Miami. He was made the fall guy for the animal relocation fiasco and was fired immediately by Half-Moon Enterprises, a company trying to appear more "environmentally friendly."

Ollie was given probation for stealing the nursery truck. His help in freeing the animals and exposing the scheme of his former employers helped him gain hero status. He was later hired by WBRD news where he is an analyst and follows the developments surrounding the Everglades, giving his expert opinion as a former insider for big business.

The animals in this story may have had happy endings, but we humans have to work together to ensure that the Everglades are protected. Everglades National Park is still a very beautiful and unique place. It is one of the great wonders of the world and is home to a variety of species of animals and plants. The health of the Everglades affects ecosystems from the mainland of Florida all the way into the Caribbean and Gulf of Mexico. It is up to people to take the steps to ensure this amazing and beautiful ecosystem is preserved and the animals are protected.

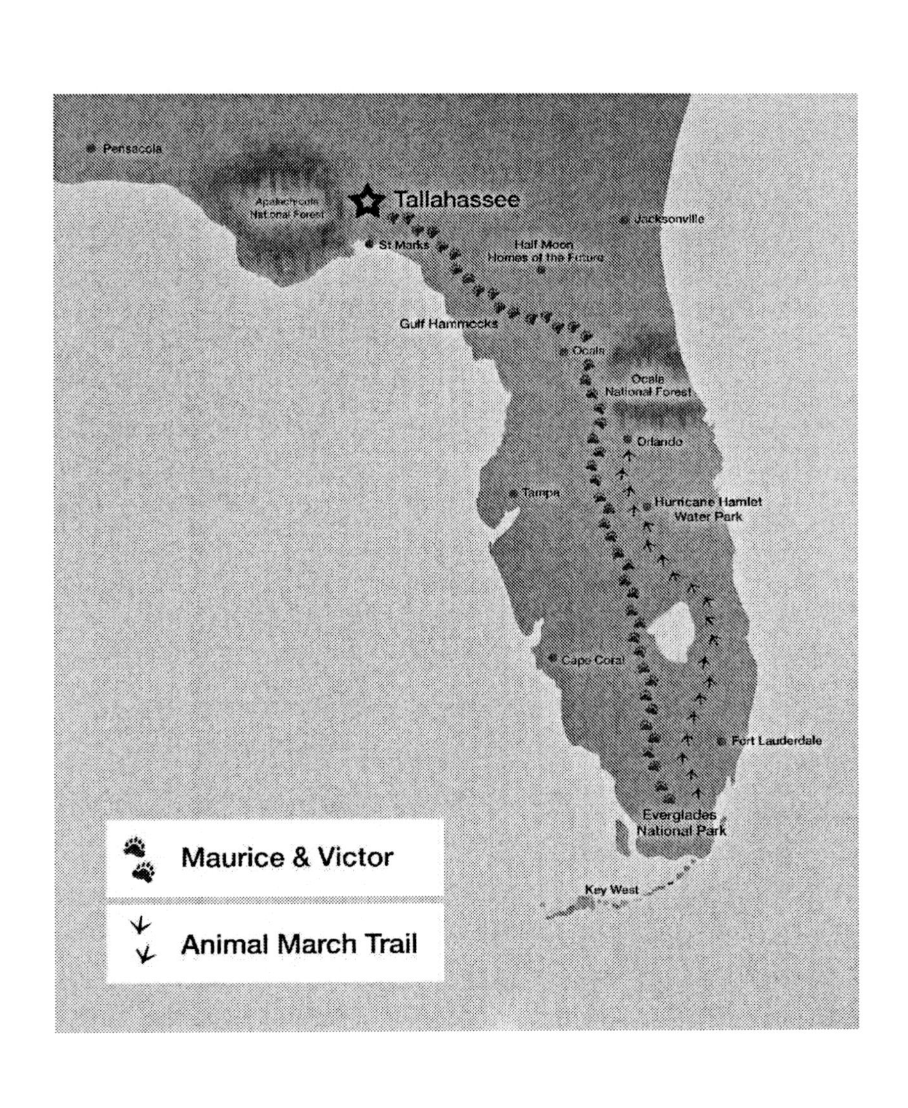
Pensacola
Tallahassee
Jacksonville
St Marks
Half Moon
Homes of the Future
Gulf Hammocks
Ocala
Ocala
National Forest
Orlando
Tampa
Hurricane Hamlet
Water Park
Cape Coral
Fort Lauderdale
Everglades
National Park
Key West
Maurice & Victor
Animal March Trail

About the Author

Kim Frances Lee is a native Floridian and the author of *Lost in the Okefenokee Swamp*, published for Newspapers in Education in 2006. She resides near the Capitol of Florida where farfetched stories occur on a regular basis. Kim has been writing about Florida and the ecosystems connected with the state since her college days at Florida State University. Growing up in central Florida, she spent many hours in the Ocala National Forest and along the Gulf Coast near Crystal River. Her characters and stories are taken from these environments and point out the beauty and the problems that tend to go hand-in-hand in a state with so many ecosystems and people. She writes her stories at her home away from home on the Forgotten Coast with the waves of the Gulf of Mexico as background music and the inspiration that keeps her focused. She is a member of the Children's Book Writers Association, Tallahassee Writers Association, The Alliance of Independent Book Writers, and The What Writer's Group. You can find out more about her stories and life at www.KimFrancesLee.com.